Revit MEP 2019
for Novices
(Learn By Doing)

CADSoft Technologies

Revit MEP 2019 for Novices:
Learn By Doing

CADSoft Technologies

CADSoft Technologies

ISBN 978-1-64057-042-9

NOTICE TO THE READER
Publisher does not warrant or guarantee any of the products described in the text or perform any independent analysis in connection with any of the product information contained in the text. Publisher does not assume, and expressly disclaims, any obligation to obtain and include information other than that provided to it by the manufacturer.

The reader is expressly warned to consider and adopt all safety precautions that might be indicated by the activities herein and to avoid all potential hazards. By following the instructions contained herein, the reader willingly assumes all risks in connection with such instructions.

The publisher makes no representation or warranties of any kind, including but not limited to, the warranties of fitness for particular purpose or merchantability, nor are any such representations implied with respect to the material set forth herein, and the publisher takes no responsibility with respect to such material. The publisher shall not be liable for any special, consequential, or exemplary damages resulting, in whole or part, from the reader's use of, or reliance upon this material.

DEDICATION

*To teachers, who make it possible to disseminate knowledge
to enlighten the young and curious minds
of our future generations*

*To students, who are dedicated to learning new technologies
and making the world a better place to live in*

THANKS

*To employees of CADCIM Technologies and
Tickoo Institute of Emererging Technologies for their valuable help*

Online Training Program Offered by CADSoft Technologies

CADSoft Technologies provides effective and affordable virtual online training on various software packages including Computer Aided Design, Manufacturing and Engineering (CAD/CAM/CAE), computer programming languages, animation, architecture, and GIS. The training is delivered 'live' via Internet at any time, any place, and at any pace to individuals as well as the students of colleges, universities, and CAD/CAM/CAE training centers. The main features of this program are:

Training for Students and Companies in a Classroom Setting

Highly experienced instructors and qualified Engineers at CADSoft Technologies conduct the classes under the guidance of Prof. Sham Tickoo of Purdue University Northwest, USA. This team has authored several textbooks that are rated "one of the best" in their categories and are used in various colleges, universities, and training centers in North America, Europe, and in other parts of the world.

Training for Individuals

CADSoft Technologies with its cost effective and time saving initiative strives to deliver the training in the comfort of your home or work place, thereby relieving you from the hassles of traveling to training centers.

Training Offered on Software Packages

CADSoft Technologies provide basic and advanced training on the following software packages:

CAD/CAM/CAE*: CATIA, Pro/ENGINEER Wildfire, SOLIDWORKS, Autodesk Inventor, Solid Edge, NX, AutoCAD, AutoCAD LT, Customizing AutoCAD, AutoCAD Electrical, EdgeCAM, and ANSYS*

Architecture and GIS*: Autodesk Revit (Architecture/Structure/MEP), Autodesk Navisworks, ETABS, Bentley STAAD.Pro, AutoCAD Raster Design, ArcGIS, AutoCAD Civil 3D, AutoCAD Map 3D, Oracle Primavera P6, MS Project*

Animation and Styling*: Autodesk 3ds Max, 3ds Max Design, Autodesk Maya, Autodesk Alias, Pixologic ZBrush, and CINEMA 4D*

Computer Programming: *C++, VB.NET, Oracle, AJAX, and Java*

Personality Development: *Personality Development and Engineering Ethics/Soft Skills Course*

Table of Contents

Chapter 2: Getting Started with an MEP Project

Chapter 3: Creating Building Envelopes

Chapter 4: Creating Spaces and Zones and Performing Load Analysis

Chapter 5: Creating an HVAC System

Chapter 6: Creating an Electrical System

Chapter 7: Creating Plumbing Systems

Preface

Revit MEP 2019

Autodesk Revit is a Building Information Modeling software designed for Architects, Structural Engineers, MEP Engineers, Designers, and Contractors. The software has the capability to design the 3D model of a building with its various components, annotate the model with 2D drafting elements, and access building information from the building model's database.

Autodesk Revit also has the capabilty of executing 4D BIM with tools to plan and track various stages in the building's lifecycle, from concept to construction and later demolition.

The MEP discipline of Revit was introduced to the users in 2006 as Revit MEP. This software is primarily used in designing the Mechanical, Electrical, and Plumbing and Piping systems, which are the three disciplines of building services. In Revit, you can create the plans, elevations, sections, schedules, and 3D models of a building project that can be easily accessed and shared between different users.

The *Revit MEP 2019 for Novices: Learn By Doing* textbook explains the concepts and principles of MEP in Revit through practical examples, tutorials, and exercises. This enables the users to harness the power of BIM with Autodesk Revit for their specific use. In this textbook, the author explains in detail the procedure of evaluating HVAC cooling and heating loads and the usage of tools required for designing HVAC, electrical, and plumbing design. In addition, in this textbook, you will learn tools and concepts for creating families and process to document the final drawings.

In this textbook, special emphasis has been laid on the concepts of space modeling and tools to create systems for all disciplines (MEP). Each concept in this textbook is explained using the detailed description and relevant graphical examples and illustrations. The accompanying tutorials and exercises, which relate to the real world projects, help you understand the usage and abilities of the tools available in Autodesk Revit. Along with the main text, the chapters have been punctuated with tips and notes to make the concepts clear, thereby enabling you to create your own innovative projects.

The main features of this textbook are as follows:

- **Tutorial Approach**

    The author has adopted the tutorial point-of-view approach and the learn-by-doing approach throughout the textbook. This approach helps the users learn the concepts and procedures easily.

- **Real-World Designs as Tutorials**

    The author has used real-world building designs and architectural examples as tutorials in this textbook so that the users can correlate them to the real-time designs.

- **Tips and Notes**

  Additional information related to various topics is provided to the users in the form of tips and notes.

- **Learning Objectives**

  The first page of every chapter summarizes the topics that will be covered in that chapter. This will help the users to easily refer to a topic.

Symbols Used in the Textbook

Note

The author has provided additional information to the users about the topic being discussed in the form of notes.

Tip

Special information and techniques are provided in the form of tips that help in increasing the efficiency of the users.

Formatting Conventions Used in the Textbook

Please refer to the following list for the formatting conventions used in this textbook.

- Names of tools, buttons, options, browser, palette, panels, and tabs are written in boldface.

  Example: The **Duct** tool, the **Modify** button, the **HVAC** panel, the **Systems** tab, **Properties** palette, **Project Browser**, and so on.

- Names of dialog boxes, drop-downs, drop-down lists, list boxes, areas, edit boxes, check boxes, and radio buttons are written in boldface.

  Example: The **Options** dialog box, the **Wire** drop-down in the **Electrical** panel of the **Systems** tab, the **Name** edit box in the **Name** dialog box, the **Chain** check box in the **Options Bar**, and so on.

- Values entered in edit boxes are written in boldface.

  Example: Enter **4"** (**100mm**) in the **Offset** edit box.

- Names of the files saved are italicized.

  Example: *c03_Office-Space_tut2.rvt*

- The methods of invoking a tool/option from the ribbon, Application Menu, or the shortcut keys are given in a shaded box.

  Ribbon: Systems > Electrical > Wire drop-down > Arc Wire
  File menu: New
  Shortcut Keys: CTRL+N

• When you select an element or a component, a contextual tab is displayed depending upon the entity selected. For example: **Modify | (Elements / Components)**.

Naming Conventions Used in the Textbook

Tool
If you click on an item in a panel of the ribbon and a command is invoked to create/edit an object or perform some action, then that item is termed as **tool**.

For example:
Duct tool, **Air Terminal** tool, **Isolated** tool
Filled Region tool, **Trim/Extend to Corner** tool, **Rotate** tool

If you click on an item in a panel of the ribbon and a dialog box is invoked wherein you can set the properties to create/edit an object, then that item is also termed as **tool**, refer to Figure 1.

For example:
Load Family tool, **Duct** tool, **Wall** tool
Plumbing Fixture tool, **Visibility/Graphic**s tool

Figure 1 Tools in the ribbon

Button
The item in a dialog box that has a 3d shape like a button is termed as **button**. For example, **OK** button, **Cancel** button, **Apply** button, and so on. If the item in a ribbon is used to exit a tool or a mode, it is also termed as button. For example, **Modify** button, **Finish Editing System** button, **Cancel Editing System** button, and so on; refer to Figure 2.

*Figure 2 Choosing the **Finish Editing System** button*

Dialog Box
In this textbook, different terms are used for referring to the components of a dialog box. Refer to Figure 3 for the terminology used.

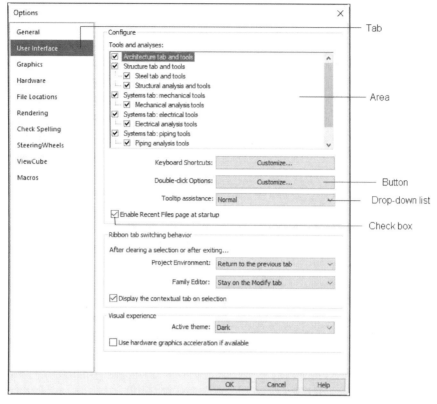

Figure 3 Components of a dialog box

Drop-down

A drop-down is the one in which a set of common tools are grouped together for creating an object. You can identify a drop-down with a down arrow on it. These drop-downs are given a name based on the tools grouped in them. For example, **Wall** drop-down, **Component** drop-down, **Region** drop-down, and so on; refer to Figure 4.

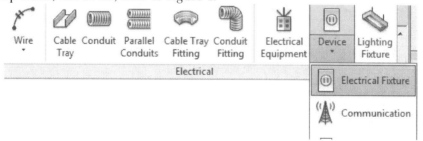

Figure 4 Choosing a tool from the drop-down

Drop-down List

A drop-down list is the one in which a set of options are grouped together. You can set various parameters using these options. You can identify a drop-down list with a down arrow on it. For example, **Type Selector** drop-down list, **Units** drop-down list, and so on; refer to Figure 5.

Options

Options are the items that are available in shortcut menus, drop-down lists, dialog boxes, and so on. For example, choose the **Zoom In Region** option from the shortcut menu displayed on right-clicking in the drawing area; refer to Figure 6.

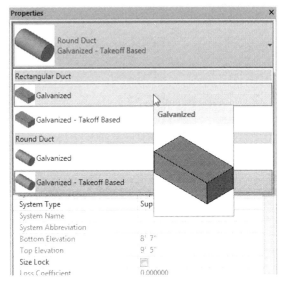

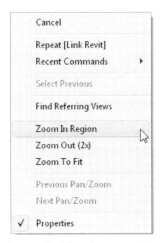

Figure 5 *Selecting an option from the **Type Selector** drop-down list*

Figure 6 *Choosing an option from the shortcut menu*

Free Companion Website

It has been our constant endeavor to provide you the best textbooks and services at affordable price. In this endeavor, we have come out with a Free Companion website that will facilitate the process of teaching and learning of Autodesk Revit 2019. If you purchase this textbook, you will get access to the files on the Companion website.

The resources available for the faculty and students in this website are as follows:

Faculty Resources
• **Technical Support**
  You can get online technical support by contacting ***techsupport@cadcim.com***.

• **Instructor Guide**
  Solutions to all review questions and exercises in the textbook are provided in this guide to help the faculty members test the skills of the students.

• **PowerPoint Presentations**
  The contents of the book are arranged in PowerPoint slides that can be used by the faculty for their lectures.

• **Revit Files**
  The Revit files (*.rvt*) used in tutorials and exercises are available for free download.

Student Resources

- **Technical Support**

  You can get online technical support by contacting ***techsupport@cadcim.com***.

- **Revit Files**

  The Revit files (*.rvt*) used in tutorials are available for free download.

- **Learning Resources**

  Additional learning resources available at *http://revitxperts.blogspot.com*.

If you face any problem in accessing these files, please contact the publisher at *sales@cadcim.com* or the author at *stickoo@pnw.edu* or *tickoo525@gmail.com*.

Stay Connected

You can now stay connected with us through Facebook and Twitter to get the latest information about our textbooks, videos, and teaching/learning resources. To stay informed of such updates, follow us on Facebook (***www.facebook.com/cadcim***) and Twitter (***@cadcimtech***). You can also subscribe to our YouTube channel (***www.youtube.com/cadcimtech***) to get the information about our latest video tutorials.

Chapter *1*

Introduction to Autodesk Revit 2019 for MEP

Learning Objectives

After completing this chapter, you will be able to:
- *Understand the basic concepts and principles of Revit for MEP*
- *Understand various terms used in Revit for MEP*
- *Describe the parametric behavior of Revit*
- *Start the Revit 2019 program*
- *Understand the interface of Revit 2019*
- *Access the Revit 2019 Help*

INTRODUCTION TO Autodesk Revit FOR MEP

Autodesk Revit is a Building Information Modeling software, which is developed for professionals in the AEC (Architecture, Engineering, and Construction) industry. Revit is used by Architects, Structural Engineers, MEP Engineers, Designers and Contractors for a building project.

The MEP functionality in Revit was introduced in 2006 as a separate software, Revit MEP. It was specifically built for MEP engineers and designers. Since then, it has become very popular in the Building Information Modeling (BIM) workflow. This software provides engineers and designers with tools for the analysis, modeling, and design of various building elements and systems for MEP (Mechanical, Electrical, and Plumbing) services. Since 2017 release of Autodesk Revit, Revit MEP has been discontinued as an individual software and the MEP functionality of this software is now available in the Revit software.

Revit is a BIM software that helps users to coordinate the documentation of MEP designs with other engineering disciplines. Its integrated parametric modeling technology is used to create the information model of a project and to collect and coordinate information across all its representations. In Autodesk Revit, drawing sheets, 2D views, 3D views, sectional view, callout details, and schedules directly represent the same building information model (BIM) as the real one does. Autodesk Revit (for MEP) is developed with an approach to bring the Mechanical, Electrical, and Plumbing engineers together under the BIM framework and make the building services system efficient and interoperable with other systems. In Revit, a designer can not only work with various pre-designed elements of different MEP disciplines but can also model customized elements and add parameters to them. This helps in modeling complex designs with various permutations. Different disciplines of Revit (for MEP) are briefly described next.

Mechanical Discipline

In the Mechanical discipline, you can develop an HVAC (Heating, Ventilation, and Air Conditioning) system, keeping in view the energy requirements of that building. The study of the energy requirements of the building is very essential for developing an efficient and cost effective design. In mechanical discipline, you can design the whole ducting network with the ventilation layout plan. You can also route the piping or ducting networks manually or generate routing solutions by using various tools in this software. In this discipline, you can also develop a Fire Suppression System.

Electrical Discipline

While working with the electrical discipline, you can design an electrical system. In this system, you can add various lighting fixtures, switches, alarms, communication devices, and more as per the requirement of the project. You can also add panels and prepare panel schedules and perform the load analysis. Further, you can connect the devices and fixtures through logical circuits.

Plumbing Discipline

In this discipline, you can design a plumbing system for a project. In the plumbing system, you can add plumbing fittings, accessories, and fixtures as per the requirement of a project. In addition, you can also design fire fighting system for a building and add fire safety components to the system.

Autodesk Revit AS A BUILDING INFORMATION MODELER (BIM)

The history of computer aided design and documentation dates back to the early 1980s when architects and engineers began using this technology for documenting their projects. Realizing its advantages, information sharing capabilities were developed, especially to share data with other consultants. This led to the development of object-based CAD systems in the early 1990s. Before the development of these systems, objects such as HVAC components, pipes, plumbing fixtures, electrical fixture, and more were stored as a non-graphical data with the assigned graphics. These systems arranged the information logically but were unable to optimize its usage in a building project. Realizing the advantages of the solid modeling tools, the mechanical and manufacturing industry professionals began using the information modeling CAD technology. This technology enabled them to extract data based on the relationship between model elements.

The Building Information Modeling (BIM) provided an alternative approach to building design, construction, and management. This approach, however, required a suitable technology to implement and reap its benefits. In such a situation, the use of parametric technology with the Building Information Modeling approach was envisaged as an ideal combination. In 1997, a group of mechanical CAD technologists began working on a new software dedicated to the building industry. They developed a software that was suitable for creating MEP projects. This led to the development of Autodesk Revit.

Autodesk Revit is a design and documentation platform in which a digital MEP model is created using the parametric elements such as HVAC system, mechanical equipment, plumbing network, fire fighting, and so on. All MEP elements have inherent characteristics, and therefore, they can be tracked, managed, and maintained by using computer.

BASIC CONCEPTS AND PRINCIPLES

Autodesk Revit enables you to envisage and develop an MEP model with actual 3D parametric elements. It provides a new approach to MEP design and implementation process. It replicates the way MEP engineers conceive the structure of an MEP system. For example, the 2D CAD platforms mostly use lines to represent all elements, as shown in Figure 1-1. However, in Autodesk Revit, you can create the MEP model of a building project using 3D elements, such as HVAC components, pipes, plumbing fixtures, electrical fixtures, as shown in Figure 1-2.

Using these 3D elements, you can visualize the MEP project with respect to its scale, volume, and proportions. This enables you to study design alternatives and develop superior quality design solutions. Autodesk Revit automates routine drafting and coordination tasks and helps in reducing errors in documentation. This, in turn, saves time, improves the speed of documentation, and lowers the cost for the users.

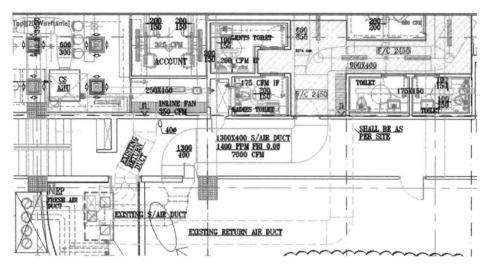

Figure 1-1 CAD project created using 2D lines

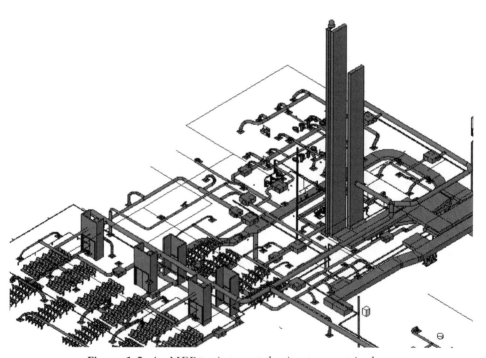

Figure 1-2 An MEP project created using parametric elements

Understanding the Parametric Building Modeling Technology

A project in Autodesk Revit is created using the inbuilt parametric building elements. The term 'parametric' refers to parameters that define relationship between various building elements. Some of these relationships are defined by Autodesk Revit itself and others by the users. For example, the relationship between air terminals and ceilings are defined by MEP and the relationship between connectors and ducts are defined by the users.

In an MEP project, each element has inbuilt bidirectional associativity with many other elements. These elements together form an integrated building information model. This model contains all data needed for the design and development of the project. You can then use this data to create project presentation views such as ceiling plans, sections, elevations, and so on for documentation. As you modify the model while working in certain views, Autodesk Revit's parametric change engine automatically updates other views. This capability is, therefore, the underlying concept in Autodesk Revit.

Autodesk Revit's parametric change engine enables you to modify design elements at any stage of the project development. As changes in the model are reflected immediately and automatically in the project, the time and effort required in coordinating the changes in other views is saved. This feature provides immense flexibility in the design and development process along with an error-free documentation.

Autodesk Revit also provides a variety of in-built parametric element libraries that can be selected and used to create a building model. It also provides you with the flexibility to modify the properties of these elements or to create your own parametric elements, based on the project requirement.

Terms Used in Autodesk Revit for MEP

Before working with Autodesk Revit, it is important to understand the basic terms used for creating a building model. Various terms in Autodesk Revit such as project, level, category, family, type, and instance are described next.

Autodesk Revit Project

A project in Autodesk Revit is similar to an actual project. In an actual project, the entire documentation such as drawings, 3D views, specifications, schedules, cost estimates, and so on are inherently linked and read together. Similarly, in Autodesk Revit, a project not only includes the digital 3D MEP model but also its parametrically associated documentation. Thus, all the components such as the building model and its standard views, MEP drawings, and schedules together form a complete project. A project file contains all the project information such as building and MEP elements used in a project, drawing sheets, schedules, cost estimates, 3D views, renderings, and so on. A project file also stores various settings such as environment, lighting, and so on. As the entire data is stored in the same file, so it becomes easier for Autodesk Revit to coordinate the database.

Levels in a Building Model

In Autodesk Revit, a building model is divided into different levels. These levels may be understood as infinite horizontal planes that act as hosts for different elements such as roof, floor, ceiling, and so on. Each element that you create belongs to a particular level.

Subdivisions of Elements into Categories and Subcategories

Apart from MEP elements, an Autodesk Revit project also contains other associated elements such as annotations, imported files, links, and so on. These elements have been divided into the following categories:

Model Category	:	Consists of various MEP elements such as HVAC elements, ducts, air terminals, diffusers, pipes, plumbing fixtures, electrical conduits, and others used in creating systems
Annotation Category	:	Consists of annotations such as dimensions, text notes, tags, symbols, and so on
Datum Category	:	Consists of datums such as levels, grids, reference planes, and so on
View Category	:	Consists of interactive project views such as the architectural, mechanical, and plumbing floor plans, elevations, sections, 3D views, and renderings

In addition to these four categories, other categories such as **Imported**, **Workset**, **Filter**, and **Revit Categories** can also exist if the project has imported files, enabled worksets, or linked Autodesk Revit projects, respectively.

Families in Autodesk Revit

Another powerful concept in Autodesk Revit is family. A family is described as a set of elements of the same category that are grouped together based on certain common parameters or characteristics. Elements of the same family may have different properties, but they all have common characteristics. For example, **Rectangular Diffuser - Round Connection** is an air diffuser family and it contains different sizes of air diffusers. Family files have the *.rfa* extension. You can load additional MEP component families from the libraries provided in Autodesk Revit package.

Families are further divided into certain types. A type or family type, as it is called, is a specific size or style of a family. For example, **Rectangular Diffuser - Round Connection 24x24 - 10 Neck** in Metric (**M_Rectangular Diffuser - Round Connection 600x600- 230 Neck**) is an air diffuser type. Family and family types can also be used to create new families using the **Family Editor**.

Instances are the actual usage of model elements in an MEP model or annotations in a drawing sheet. A family type, created at a new location, is identified as an instance of the family type. All the instances of the same family type have the same properties. Therefore, when you modify the properties of a family type, the properties of all its instances also get modified. The family categorization of Revit elements is given below:

Model Category	: Air diffuser
Family	: **Rectangular Diffuser - Round Connection**
Family type	: **Rectangular Diffuser - Round Connection 24x24 - 10 Neck**
Instance	: Particular usage of a family type

The hierarchy of service elements in Autodesk Revit plays an important role in providing flexibility and ease in managing a change in a building model. Figure 1-3 shows the hierarchy of categories and families in a typical Autodesk Revit project.

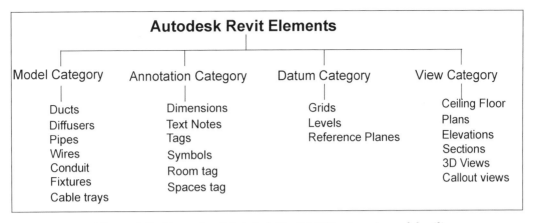

Figure 1-3 *Hierarchy of Autodesk Revit MEP categories and families*

Creating an MEP Model Using Parametric Elements

Another classification of categories of elements followed in Autodesk Revit is based on their usage. Autodesk Revit uses five classes of elements: Host, component, annotation, view, and datum. Hosts are the element categories that form the basic system of an MEP model and include model elements such as ducts, pipes, cables, and more. Components are the elements that are added to host elements or act as stand-alone elements such as air terminals, diffusers, and conduits, as shown in Figure 1-4. Annotations are the 2D, view-specific elements such as dimensions, tags, text notes, and so on that add content to the project documentation. Views represent various orientations of a building model such as plans, elevations, sections, 3D views, and so on. Datum refers to the reference elements that assist you in creating a building model, which include grids, levels, reference planes, and so on.

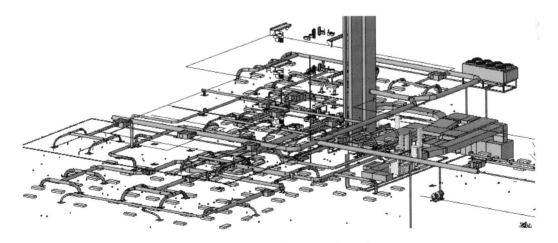

Figure 1-4 *Mechanical system with its elements*

Visibility/Graphics Overrides, Scale, and Detail Level

Autodesk Revit enables you to control the display and graphic representation of a single element or the element category of various elements in the project views. This is done by using the visibility and graphics overrides tools. You can select a model category and modify its linetype and detail level. This can also be done for various annotation category elements and imported files. These settings can be done for each project view based on its desired representation. You can also hide an element or an element category in a view using the **Hide in view** and **Isolate** tools. You can override the graphic representation of an element or an element category in any view using the **Visibility/Graphics** tool.

The scale is another important concept in an Autodesk Revit project. You can set the scale for each project view by selecting it from the available list of standard scales such as **1/16"=1'0"**, **1/4"=1'0"**, **1"=1'0"**, **1/2"=1'0"** for Imperial system or **1: 50**, **1: 100**, **1: 200**, **1: 500** for Metric system. As you set a scale, Autodesk Revit automatically sets the detail level that is appropriate for it. There are three detail levels provided in an Autodesk Revit project: **Coarse**, **Medium**, and **Fine**. You can also set the detail level manually for each project view. Each detail level has an associated linetype and the detail lines associated with it. The details of annotations, such as dimensions, tags, and so on, are also defined by the selected scale.

Extracting Project Information

A single integrated building information is used to create and represent a building project. You can extract project information from a building model and create area schemes, schedule, and cost estimates, and then add them to the project presentation.

Creating an MEP Drawing Set

After creating the building model, you can easily arrange the project views by plotting them on the drawing sheets. The drawing sheets can also be organized in a project file based on the established CAD standards followed by the firm. In this manner, the project documentation can easily be transformed from the conceptual design stage to the design development stage and finally to the construction document stage. The project view on a drawing sheet is only a graphical representation of the building information model. Therefore, any modification in it is immediately made in all associated project views, keeping the drawing set always updated.

Creating an Unusual Building Geometry

Autodesk Revit also helps you conceptualize a building project in terms of its volume, shape, and proportions before working with actual building elements. This is done by using the **Massing** tool, which enables you to create quick 3D models of buildings and conduct volumetric and proportion study on overall masses. It also enables you to visualize and create an unusual building geometry. The same massing model can then be converted into a building model with individual parametric building elements. It provides continuity to the generation of building model right from sketch design to its development. You can also create various custom MEP elements as per the project requirement and then load them to the project.

Flexibility of Creating Special Elements

Autodesk Revit provides a large number of in-built family types of various model elements and annotations. Each parametric element has the associated properties that can be modified based on the project requirement.

Autodesk Revit also enables you to create the elements that are designed specifically for a particular location. The in-built family editor enables you to create new elements using family templates. This provides you with the flexibility of using in-built elements for creating your own elements. For example, using the furniture template, you can create a reception desk that is suitable for a particular location in the design.

Creating Services Layouts

Autodesk Revit provides you with an extensive in-built library of MEP elements that can be used to add elements such as ducts, air terminals, diffusers, conduits, and so on to a project. This helps MEP consultants to include these service elements in the basic architectural building model and check for inconsistency, if any.

Working on Large Projects

In Autodesk Revit, you can work on large projects by linking different building projects together. For a large project that comprises of a number of buildings, you can create individual buildings as separate projects and then link all of them into a single base file. The database recognizes the linked projects and includes them in the project representation of the base file.

For example, while working on a large educational institution campus, you can create separate project files for academic building, administration area, gymnasium, cafeteria, computer center, and so on, and then link them into the base site plan file. In this manner, large projects can be subdivided and worked upon simultaneously.

Working in Large Teams and Coordinating with Consultants

In Autodesk Revit, worksets enable the division of the MEP model into small editable sets of disciplines such as Mechanical, Electrical, and Plumbing. The worksets can be assigned to different teams working on the same project and then their work can easily be coordinated by sharing the files in the central file location. The effort required to coordinate, collaborate, and communicate the changes between various worksets is taken care of by the computer. Various consultants working on a project can be assigned a workset with a set of editable elements. They can then incorporate their services and modify the associated elements.

For example, a high rise commercial building project can be divided into different worksets with independent teams working on different disciplines such as Mechanical, Electrical, Plumbing, Architecture, Structure, and so on. The structural consultants can be assigned to the exterior skin and the core workset, in which they can incorporate structural elements. Similarly, the rest of the teams can work independently on different worksets.

STARTING Autodesk Revit 2019

You can start Autodesk Revit by double-clicking on the **Revit 2019** icon on the desktop. Alternatively, choose **All Programs > Autodesk > Revit 2019 > Revit 2019**, from the **Start** menu (for Windows 7); the user interface screen is displayed, as shown in Figure 1-5.

Note
The path for starting Autodesk Revit depends on the operating system being used.

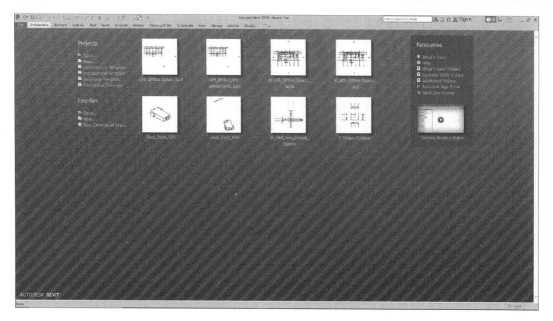

Figure 1-5 *The interface of Autodesk Revit 2019*

USER INTERFACE

In Autodesk Revit, the user interface consists of the Ribbon, Drawing area, Properties palette, Status Bar, and the View Control Bar, as shown in Figure 1-6. In Autodesk Revit, all the tools are grouped in several panels in the ribbon.

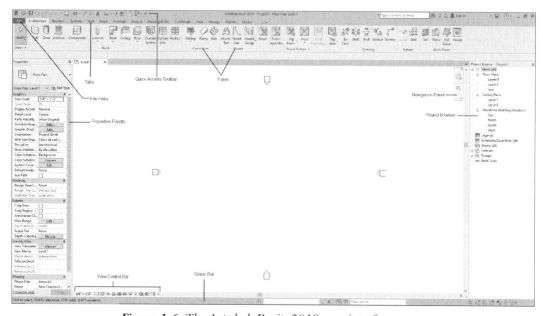

Figure 1-6 *The Autodesk Revit 2019 user interface screen*

The following table gives description of various tabs in ribbon.

Tab	Description
Architecture	Contains tools for creating an architectural model
Structure	Contains tools for creating structural model
Systems	Contains tools for creating an MEP model
Steel	Contains tools for the modification of the steel structure
Insert	Contains tools for inserting or managing secondary files such as raster image files and CAD files
Annotate	Contains tools for documenting a building model such as adding texts and dimensions
Analyze	Contains tools for analyzing the structural model
Massing & Site	Contains tools for creating massing and site elements
Collaborate	Contains tools for collaborating the project with other team members (internal and external)
View	Contains tools for managing and modifying the current views, switching views, and so on.
Manage	Contains tools for specifying the project and system parameters and settings
Add - Ins	Contains add in links for interoperability of BIM software
Modify	Contains tools for editing elements in the model

Application Frame

The application frame helps you manage projects in Autodesk Revit. It consists of **File** menu, **Quick Access Toolbar**, **InfoCenter**, and **Status Bar**. These are discussed next.

File Menu

The **File** menu contains the tools that provide access to tools such as **Open**, **Close**, and **Save**, as shown in Figure 1-7. Alternatively, press ALT+F to display tools in the **File** menu.

*Figure 1-7 The **File** menu*

Quick Access Toolbar

The **Quick Access Toolbar**, shown in Figure 1-8, contains the options to undo and redo changes, open and save a file, create a new file, and so on.

By default, the **Quick Access Toolbar** contains the options such as **Open**, **Save**, **Redo**, **Undo**, and so on. You can customize the display of the **Quick Access Toolbar** by adding more tools and removing the unwanted tools. To add a tool or a button from the panel of the ribbon to the **Quick Access Toolbar**, place the cursor over the button; the button will be highlighted. Next, right-click; a flyout will be displayed. Choose **Add to Quick Access Toolbar** from the flyout displayed; the highlighted button will be added to the **Quick Access Toolbar**. The **Quick Access Toolbar** can be customized to reorder the tools displayed in it. To do so, choose the down arrow next to the **Switch Windows** drop-down in the **Quick Access Toolbar**, refer to Figure 1-8; a flyout will be displayed. Choose the **Customize Quick Access Toolbar** option located at the bottom of the flyout; the **Customize Quick Access Toolbar** dialog box will be displayed. Use various options in this dialog box to customize the display of toolbar and choose the **OK** button; the **Customize Quick Access Toolbar** dialog box will close and the tools in the **Quick Access Toolbar** will be reordered.

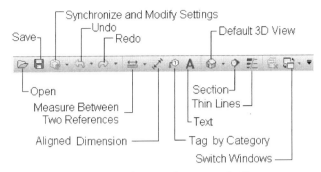

*Figure 1-8 The **Quick Access Toolbar***

InfoCenter

You can use **InfoCenter** to search for information related to Revit (Help) to display the **Subscription Center** panel for subscription services and product updates, and to display the **Favorites** panel to access saved topics. Figure 1-9 displays various tools in **InfoCenter**.

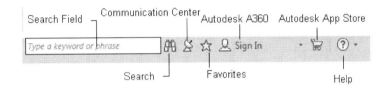

*Figure 1-9 The **InfoCenter***

Status Bar

The Status Bar is located at the bottom of the interface screen. When the cursor is placed over an element or a component, the Status Bar displays the name of the family and the type of the corresponding element or components. It also displays prompts and messages to help you use the selected tools.

View Control Bar

The **View Control Bar** is located at the lower left corner of the drawing window, as shown in Figure 1-10. It can be used to access various view-related tools. The **Scale** button shows the scale of the current view. When you can choose this button, a flyout containing standard drawing scales is displayed. From this flyout, you can then select the scale for the current view. The **Detail Level** button is used to set the detail level of a view. You can select the required detail level as **Coarse**, **Medium**, and **Fine**. Similarly, the **Visual Style** button enables you to set the display style. The options for setting the display style are: **Wireframe**, **Hidden Line**, **Shaded**, **Consistent Colors**, **Shaded**, and **Raytrace**.

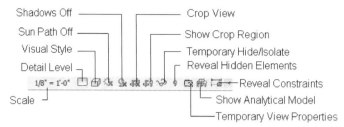

Figure 1-10 The View Control Bar

Options Bar

The **Options Bar** provides information about the common parameters of a component type. It also displays options for creating or editing them. The options displayed in the **Options Bar** change according to the type of component being created and selected for editing. Figure 1-11 displays the options in the **Options Bar** to create a structural column.

*Figure 1-11 The **Options Bar** with different options to create a duct*

Type Selector

The **Type Selector** drop-down list is located in the **Properties** palette for the currently invoked tool. On invoking the **Duct** tool, the properties of the duct will be displayed in the **Properties** palette. In this palette, you can use the **Type Selector** drop-down list to select the required type of the beam. The options in the **Type Selector** drop-down list keep changing, depending upon the current function of the tool or the elements selected. The **Type Selector** drop-down list can also be used to specify the type of an element or component while placing that element or the component in a drawing by using the **Place a Component** tool. You can also use this drop-down list to change the type of a selected element.

Drawing Area

The Drawing Area is the actual modeling area where you can create and view the building model. It covers the major portion of the interface screen. You can draw building components in this area. The position of the pointing device is represented by the cursor. The Drawing Area also has the standard Microsoft Windows functions and buttons such as close, minimize, maximize, scroll bar, and so on. These buttons have the same function as that of the other Microsoft Windows-based programs.

PROJECT BROWSER

The **Project Browser** is located below the ribbon. It displays project views, schedules, sheets, families, and groups in a logical, tree-like structure, as shown in Figure 1-12 and helps you to open and manage them. To open a view, double-click on the name of the view, or drag and drop the view in the Drawing Area. You can close the **Project Browser** or dock it anywhere in the Drawing Area.

Note
*If the **Project Browser** is not displayed on the screen, choose the **View** tab from the ribbon and then select the **Project Browser** check box from **View** > **Windows** > **User Interface** drop-down.*

The **Project Browser** can be organized to group the views and sheets based on the project requirement. For example, while working on a large project with a number of sheets, you can organize the **Project Browser** to view and access specific sheets.

Note

*In the **Project Browser**, you can expand or contract the view listing by selecting the '+' or '-' sign, respectively. The current view in the drawing window is highlighted in bold letters. The default project file has a set of preloaded views.*

Keyboard Accelerators

In Autodesk Revit, accelerator keys have been assigned to some of the frequently used tools. These keys are shortcuts that you can type from the keyboard to invoke the corresponding tool. The accelerator key corresponding to a tool appears as a tooltip when you move the cursor over the tool.

Properties Palette

The **Properties** palette, as shown in Figure 1-13, is an interface without model, which displays the type and element properties of various elements and views in a drawing.

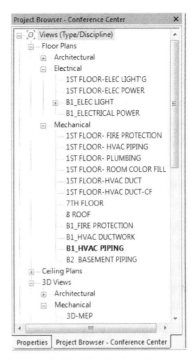

*Figure 1-12 The **Project Browser***

*Figure 1-13 The **Properties** palette*

DIALOG BOXES

Some Autodesk Revit tools, when invoked, display a dialog box. A dialog box is an interface for accessing, specifying, and modifying the parameters related to that tool. For example, when you choose **Save As > Project** from the **File** menu, the **Save As** dialog box is displayed, as shown in Figure 1-14.

A dialog box consists of various parts such as dialog label, radio buttons, text or edit boxes, check boxes, slider bars, image box, buttons, and tools, which are similar to other windows-based programs. Some dialog boxes contain the **Browse** button, which displays another related dialog box. There are certain buttons such as **OK**, **Cancel**, and **Help**, which appear at the bottom of most of the dialog boxes. The names of the buttons imply their respective functions.

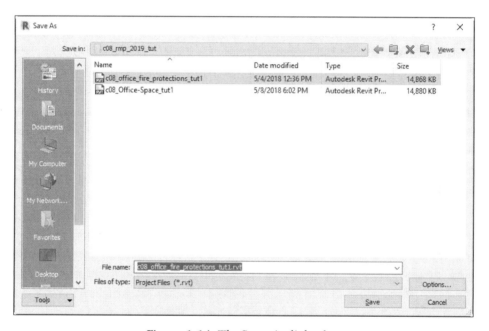

*Figure 1-14 The **Save As** dialog box*

INTEROPERABILITY OF Autodesk Revit

The models or geometries created in Autodesk Revit can be easily exported to AutoCAD and AutoCAD Architecture in the DWG file format. This enables structural engineers to collaborate with Architects. One of the important aspects of the job of a structural engineer is to collaborate and share information with the rest of the design team including the architect. To facilitate this requirement, Revit 2019 follows a wide range of industry standards and supports various CAD file formats such as *DWF, DGN, DWG, DGN, IFC, SKP*, and *SAT*. For image files, it supports *JPG, TIFF, BMP, PNG, AVI, PAN, IVR*, and *TGA* file formats. Besides these, the formats that are supported by Revit include *ODBC, HTML, TXT, XML, XLS*, and *MDB*. Autodesk Revit is compatible with any CAD system that supports the DWG, DXF, or DGN file format. Revit can import the models and geometries as ACIS solids. This enables engineers to import models from AutoCAD Architecture and AutoCAD MEP (Mechanical, Electrical, and Plumbing) software and to link the 3D information to Revit. This feature makes Autodesk Revit 2019 an efficient, user-friendly, and compatible software.

WORKSHARING USING REVIT SERVER

Worksharing is a method of distributing work among people involved in a project to accomplish it within the stipulated period of time. In worksharing, each person involved in the project is assigned a task that has to be accomplished through proper planning and coordination with the other members of the team. In a large scale building project, worksharing helps in finishing a project in time and meeting the quality requirements that are set during the process. Generally, in a large scale building project, the professionals such as structural engineers, architects, interior architects, and MEP engineers are involved in their respective fields to accomplish the project. So, the distribution of work at the primary stage is made on the basis of the area of specialization. Each professional has his own set of work to perform for the accomplishment of the project. Therefore, worksharing is an important process that is required to be implemented efficiently to complete the project in time. In Autodesk Revit, you can apply server-based worksharing with the help of Revit Server which is a server application. Revit Server uses a central server and multiple local servers for collaborating across a Wide Area Network (WAN). The central server hosts the central model of a workshared project and remains accessible to all the team members over the Wide Area Network. Similarly, the local server is accessible to all team members in a Local Area Network (LAN). The local server hosts a local updated copy of the central model. In the Worksharing environment, the team members are not aware of the local server, as it is transparent in their daily operations. Refer to Figure 1-15 for the network model of Revit Server.

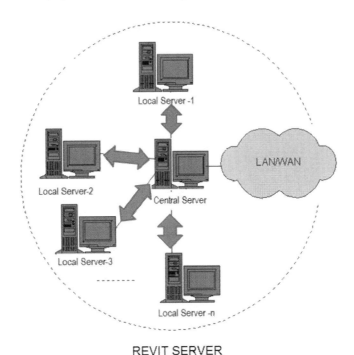

Figure 1-15 The network model of Revit Server

Autodesk Revit HELP

In Autodesk Revit, you can access various help topics online by using the **Autodesk Revit 2019** help page. You can access this page by choosing the **Help** tool from the **InfoCenter**, refer to Figure 1-16. In this page, different areas such as **Learn about Revit**, **Resources**, and others are displayed. You can click on the required link from these areas to get the related information. In the **Learn about Revit** area, various help options related to Autodesk Revit are available. You can click on the required option to display the help page corresponding to the option. The **Resources** area contains various learning resources. You can click on the desired option in this area to get the information related to it.

Figure 1-16 The **AUTODESK REVIT 2019** page

Chapter 2

Getting Started with an MEP Project

After completing this chapter, you will be able to:

- *Start a new project*
- *Set the units of various measurement parameters in a project*
- *Understand the concept of snaps*
- *Save a project*
- *Use the Options dialog box*
- *Close and exit an MEP project*
- *Open an existing project*

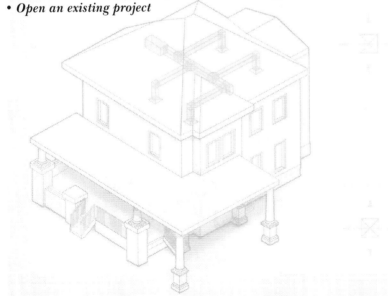

OVERVIEW OF A BIM-MEP PROJECT

In BIM environment, a project is delivered as an integrated model comprising elements of various disciplines such as Architecture, Mechanical, Electrical, Plumbing, Structure, and Coordination. This means that the project file that you create will contain all the information related to building design from geometry to various construction documentations such as schedules and legends. Generally, this information includes the details of the building elements like walls, doors, windows, beams, columns, ducts, pipes, equipment, fixtures, and others. The information in the project also includes different views of the project, working drawings created from the building elements, and the documentation related to design of the model.

In Revit, you can generate different views such as plan, elevation, and sections from a 3D building project. These views are associative in nature which means when you change the building design in one view, it is propagated throughout the project.

In Revit, the project file in which you will create the MEP project is based on a Revit Template File (*.rte*). This template provides initial settings for the project such as its units, material used, and display settings. You can customize the default settings of a project as required. The basic template file has predefined information and settings for a project.

Generally, each organization has its own standard of working in a building project. Based on the standard, a user can customize the template and then save it for further use.

> **Tip**
> *It is recommended to follow a slower approach to set up a project and give more time to create the standard template for practice and to organize the structure of the required components in a project. This helps in carrying out the project smoothly and efficiently.*

STARTING A NEW MEP PROJECT

File Menu: New > Project
Shortcut Key: CTRL+N

To start a new MEP project in Revit 2019, choose **All Programs > Autodesk > Revit 2019 > Revit 2019** from the **Start** menu (for Windows 7) or double-click on the Revit 2019 icon available on desktop; the Autodesk Revit interface will be displayed. Next, choose **New > Project** from the **File** menu, as shown in Figure 2-1; the **New Project** dialog box will be displayed, as shown in Figure 2-2.

Figure 2-1 *Choosing the* **Project** *option from the* **File** *menu*

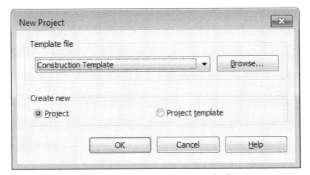

Figure 2-2 *The* **New Project** *dialog box*

In this dialog box, the **Construction Template** option is selected by default in the drop-down list in the **Template file** area. As a result, the new project will adopt the settings of the *Construction-Default* template file. Alternatively, you can select any of the following options from the drop-down list in the **Template file** area: **Architectural Template**, **Structural Template**, **Mechanical Template**, and **<None>**.

Note
The selection of the option from the drop-down list depends on the MEP discipline or discipline that you are going to work within the project.

Tip

*For an MEP project, it is recommended to start with the **Systems.rte** template file. To use this file, you need to select the **Systems Template** option from the drop-down list in the **Template file** area of the **New Project** dialog box. The **Systems.rte** template file provides a useful set up for all the disciplines such as Mechanical, Electrical, and Plumbing.*

PROJECT UNITS

Ribbon:	Manage > Settings > Project Units
Shortcut Key:	UN

Units are important parameters of a project as they provide a standard of measurement for different entities. While installing Revit, you are prompted to set the Imperial (feet and inches) or Metric (meter) unit as the default unit system. Setting a default unit system helps you start your project with a specific type of unit. To set units, choose the **Project Units** tool from the **Settings** panel; the **Project Units** dialog box will be displayed, as shown in Figure 2-3. Under the **Units** column in this dialog box, you can specify various units that are relevant to the building project.

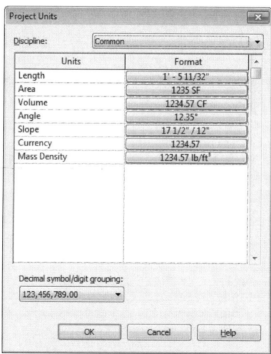

*Figure 2-3 The **Project Units** dialog box*

In the **Project Units** dialog box, units are grouped into six disciplines: **Common**, **Structural**, **HVAC**, **Electrical**, **Piping**, and **Energy**. Each discipline has a set of measurement parameters. You can select any of these disciplines from the **Discipline** drop-down list in the **Project Units** dialog box. The **Format** column in this dialog box displays the current unit format for the corresponding parameter in the **Units** column. You can preview and select the possible digit grouping and decimal separators from the **Decimal symbol/digit grouping** drop-down list, which is at the lower left corner of the dialog box. Some of the disciplines that are used in MEP projects are discussed next.

Note

*The values for different parameters displayed in the **Format** column of the **Project Units** dialog box may differ depending upon the type of unit system, Imperial or Metric, selected for the project. In this textbook, the Imperial unit system has been used in the tutorials and illustrations.*

Common Unit Type

The **Common** unit type used in an MEP project includes the parameters such as length, volume, angle, slope, and so on. In the **Project Units** dialog box, the **Common** option is selected by default in the **Discipline** drop-down list, refer to Figure 2-3. The **Common** unit type used in Revit is similar to that used in other Revit platforms. Moreover, the settings of the parameters of common units are similar to those used in other CAD programs. The methods of setting various parameters under the **Common** unit type are discussed next.

HVAC Unit Type

HVAC units are commonly used while working in the Mechanical discipline of an MEP Project. Some of the frequently used HVAC units are Density, Power, Pressure, Velocity, Air Flow, and more. In Revit, you can set the HVAC units in the **Project Units** dialog box. To do so, select the **HVAC** option from the **Discipline** drop-down list in the **Project Units** dialog box, as shown in Figure 2-4. Some of the important HVAC units are discussed next.

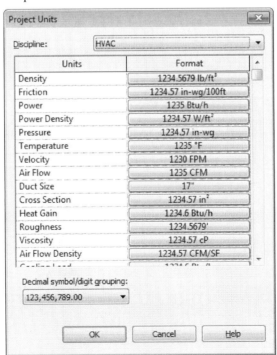

*Figure 2-4 The **Project Units** dialog box with the **HVAC** option selected in the **Discipline** drop-down list*

Setting the Unit for Power

To specify the unit for the power used for various HVAC units, click on the field corresponding to the **Power** parameter in the **Format** column; the **Format** dialog box will be displayed. In this dialog box, specify a unit by selecting the required option from the **Units** drop-down list. The **Units** drop-down list contains the options such as **Watts, Kilowatts, BTU (British Thermal Units) per second, BTU (British Thermal Units) per hour**, and so on. For the **Imperial** unit setting, **BTU (British Thermal Units) per hour** is the default option selected in the drop-down list. For the **Metric** unit setting, **Watts** is the default option selected in the drop-down list.

Setting the Unit for Pressure

The pressure in an HVAC system implies the static pressure of the system and of the air flowing inside the duct. To specify unit for the pressure, click on the field corresponding to the **Pressure** parameter in the **Format** column of the **Project Units** dialog box; the **Format** dialog box will be displayed. In this dialog box, specify the desired unit by selecting an option from the **Units** drop-down list. The **Units** drop-down list contains options such as **Inches of water(60 °F)**, **Pascals, Kilopascals, Megapascals, Bars**, and so on. The default unit selected for the **Imperial** unit setting in the drop-down list is **Inches of water(60 °F)**. The default unit selected for the **Metric** unit setting in the drop-down list is **Pascals**.

Setting the Unit for Air Flow

The **Air Flow** parameter specifies the flow rate of the air flowing in the ducts in an HVAC system. In Autodesk Revit, to set the unit for the **Air Flow** parameter, choose the button corresponding to this parameter in the **Project Units** dialog box; the **Format** dialog box will be displayed. In this dialog box, you can select various options such as **Cubic feet per minute, Liters per second, Cubic meters per second**, and so on. The default unit selected for the **Imperial** unit system for this parameter is **Cubic feet per minute**. The default unit selected for the **Metric** unit setting in the drop-down list is **Liters per second**.

Setting the Unit for Heating Load

The **Heating Load** parameter specifies the heating load of the space for which the HVAC system has to be designed. To set the unit for the **Heating Load** parameter, choose the button corresponding to this parameter in the **Project Units** dialog box; the **Format** dialog box will be displayed. In this dialog box, you can select any option such as **Watts, Kilowatts, BTU (British Thermal Units) per second, BTU (British Thermal Units) per hour**. The default unit selected in the imperial unit system for this parameter is **BTU (British Thermal Units) per hour**. For the **Metric** unit setting, **Watts** is the default option selected in the drop-down list.

Electrical Unit Type

Electrical units are commonly used while working in the Electrical discipline of an MEP Project. Some of the frequently used Electrical units are Current, Electrical Potential, Frequency, Illuminance, and more. To specify these units, invoke the **Project Units** dialog box and then select the **Electrical** option from the **Discipline** drop-down list. Some of the frequently used Electrical units are discussed next.

Setting the Unit for Illuminance

The Illuminance in an Electrical system refers to the measurement of the illumination of the surface. To specify unit for the illuminance, click on the field corresponding to the **Illuminance** parameter in the **Format** column of the **Project Units** dialog box; the **Format** dialog box will be displayed. In this dialog box, specify the desired unit for the illuminance by selecting an option from the **Units** drop-down list. The **Units** drop-down list contains two options **Footcandles** and **Lux**. The default unit selected for the **Imperial** unit setting in the drop-down list is **Footcandles**. For the **Metric** unit setting, **Lux** is the default option selected in the drop-down list.

Setting the Unit for Electrical Potential

In the Electrical discipline, the Electrical Potential refers to the potential difference of two points in the distribution. Generally, it is the voltage of the electrical supply to the equipment. In Autodesk Revit, to set the unit for the **Electrical Potential** parameter, choose the button corresponding to this parameter in the **Project Units** dialog box; the **Format** dialog box will be displayed. In this dialog box, you can select the required option from the various options provided such as **Volts**, **Kilovolts**, and **Millivolts**. The default unit selected in the **Imperial** and **Metric** unit systems is **Volts**.

Setting the Unit for Demand Factor

The Demand factor for an electrical system is the ratio of the maximum electrical load required in given time period to the maximum possible electrical load available. In Autodesk Revit, to set the unit for the **Demand Factor** parameter, choose the button corresponding to this parameter in the **Project Units** dialog box; the **Format** dialog box will be displayed. From this dialog box, you can select any of the two available options: **Percentage** and **Fixed**. The default unit selected for the **Imperial** and **Metric** unit systems is **Percentage**.

Piping Unit Type

Piping units include units for Density, Flow rate, Pressure, Velocity, and so on. In Revit, you can set the piping units in the **Project Units** dialog box. To do so, select the **Piping** option from the **Discipline** drop-down list in the **Project Units** dialog box. Some of the piping units are discussed next.

Setting the Unit for Flow

The flow in the piping system implies the flow rate of the water or fluids. To specify unit for flow, click on the field corresponding to the **Flow** parameter in the **Format** column of the **Project Units** dialog box; the **Format** dialog box will be displayed. In this dialog box, specify the desired unit for the flow by selecting an option from the **Units** drop-down list. The **Units** drop-down list contains options such as **US gallons per minute**, **US gallons per hour**, **Cubic meters per hour**, and so on. The default unit selected for the **Imperial** unit setting in the drop-down list is **US gallons per minute**. For the **Metric** unit setting, **Liters per second** is the default option selected in the drop-down list.

Setting the Unit for Velocity

The velocity in the piping system implies the velocity of water or fluids. To specify unit for velocity, click on the field corresponding to the **Velocity** parameter in the **Format** column of the **Project Units** dialog box; the **Format** dialog box will be displayed. In this dialog box, specify the desired unit for the flow by selecting an option from the **Units** drop-down list. The **Units** drop-down list contains options such as **Feet per second** and **Meters per second**. The default unit selected for the **Imperial** unit setting in the drop-down list is **Feet per second**. For the **Metric** unit setting, **Meters per second** is the default option selected in the drop-down list.

Setting the Unit for Pipe Size

The pipe size in the piping system implies the size of the pipes used in the piping distribution system. To specify unit for pipe size, click on the field corresponding to the **Pipe Size** parameter in the **Format** column of the **Project Units** dialog box; the **Format** dialog box will be displayed. In this dialog box, specify the desired unit for the pipe size by selecting an option from the **Units** drop-down list. The **Units** drop-down list contains options such as **Fractional inches**, **Decimal inches**, **Decimal feet**, and more. The default unit selected for the Imperial unit setting in the drop-down list is **Fractional inches**. For the **Metric** unit setting, **Millimeters** is the default option selected in the drop-down list.

SNAPS TOOL

Ribbon:	Manage > Settings > Snaps

The **Snaps** tool is one of the important tools used to snap elements in an MEP model. This tool is used to make the cursor snap or jump depending on the preset increments or on the specific object properties of elements such as endpoint and midpoint of elements. When you invoke the **Snaps** tool from the **Settings** panel of the **Manage** tab, the **Snaps** dialog box is displayed. This dialog box has three areas, **Dimension Snaps**, **Object Snaps**, and **Temporary Overrides**.

Note
The settings specified in this dialog box will be applied to all the projects opened in the session and will not be saved.

SAVING AN MEP PROJECT

Before you close or exit a Revit session, it is recommended to save the project file. You can save a project file in a permanent storage device, such as a hard disk or a removable storage device like CD or USB. Also, you must save your work at regular intervals to avoid data loss due to any error in the computer's hardware or software.

Using the Save As Tool

In Revit, you can save your project file at the desired location by using the **Save As** tool. To do so, choose **Save As > Project** from the **File** menu; the **Save As** dialog box will be displayed.

In the **Save As** dialog box, the **Save in** drop-down list displays the current drive and path in which the project file will be saved. The list box below the **Save in** drop-down list displays all folders available in the current directory. The **File name** edit box is used to specify the name to be assigned to the project or file. The **Places List** area on the left of the **Save As** dialog box contains shortcuts for the folders that are frequently used.

Using the Save Tool

Once a project has been saved using the **Save As** tool, you do not need to re-enter file parameters to save it again. To save a project to the hard disk, choose the **Save** option from the **File** menu. If you are saving the project for the first time, the **Save As** dialog box will be displayed, even if you invoke the **Save** tool. Alternatively, you can save your project by choosing the **Save** button from the **Quick Access Toolbar**. As you save your project file, Revit updates it automatically without prompting you to re-enter the file name and path.

THE OPTIONS DIALOG BOX

In Autodesk Revit, you can configure global settings by using the **Options** dialog box. This dialog box can be invoked by choosing the **Options** button from the **File** menu. The **Options** dialog box, as shown in Figure 2-5, contains ten tabs: **General**, **Graphics**, **File Locations**, **Hardware**, **Rendering**, **Check Spelling**, **SteeringWheels**, **ViewCube**, **User Interface**, and **Macros**.

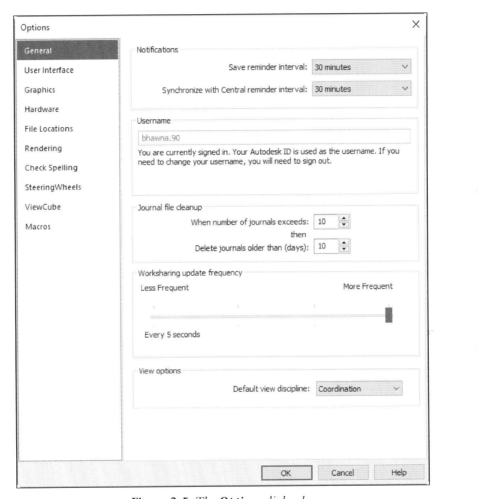

*Figure 2-5 The **Options** dialog box*

CLOSING AN MEP PROJECT

To close a project, choose the **Close** option from the **File** menu displayed. If you have already saved the latest changes, the project file will be closed. Otherwise, Revit will prompt you to save the changes using the **Save File** dialog box. You can save the changes by choosing the **Yes** button or discard them by choosing the **No** button. You can also choose the **Cancel** button to return to the interface and continue working on the project file. You can also use the **Close** button (X) in the drawing window to close the project.

EXITING AN MEP PROJECT

To exit a Revit session, choose the **Exit Revit** button from the **File** menu. Even if the project is open, you can choose the **Exit Revit** button to close the file and exit Revit. If the project has not been saved once, the **Save File** dialog box will be displayed on choosing the **Exit Revit** button. In this dialog box, if you choose the **No** button, all unsaved changes will be lost. You can also use the Close button (**X**) in the main Revit window (in the title bar) to end the Revit session.

OPENING AN EXISTING MEP PROJECT

In Autodesk Revit, there are several options available to open an existing project. The option is discussed next.

Opening an Existing Project Using the Open Tool

To open an existing project file, choose **Open > Project** from **File** menu. Alternatively, you can open the project file by choosing the **Open** button from **Quick Access Toolbar** or by pressing the CTRL+O keys. On invoking the **Open** tool, the **Open** dialog box will be displayed, as shown in Figure 2-6. Using the **Look in** drop-down list in this dialog box, you can access the desired folder and open the desired file.

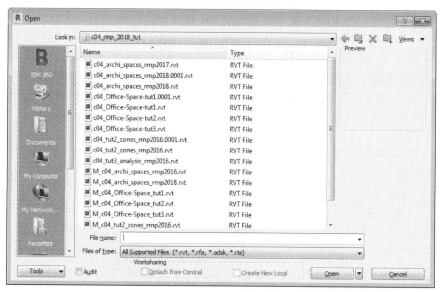

Figure 2-6 The **Open** *dialog box*

TUTORIAL

Tutorial 1   Office Space

In this tutorial, you will create a project setup for the *Office-Space* project using the following parameters and project specifications: **(Expected time: 45 min)**

1. Template file:

   For Imperial   **US Imperial > Systems-Default**

   For Metric   **US Metric > Systems-Default_Metric**

2. Project Units
3. File name to be assigned:

   For Imperial   *c02_Office-Space_tut1.rvt*

   For Metric   *M_c02_Office-Space_tut1.rvt*

The following steps are required to complete this tutorial:

a. Start the Revit 2019 session.
b. Use **Systems-Default** (Imperial) or **Systems-Default_Metric** (Metric) as the template file for the project, refer to Figure 2-8.
c. Specify the project units, refer to Figure 2-9.
d. Specify the project information, refer to Figure 2-10.
e. Create the project parameter, refer to Figure 2-11.
f. Add the project parameter to project information.
g. Set the project location.
h. Set the browser organization.
i. Save the project as *c02_Office-Space_tut1.rvt* by using the **Save As** tool.
j. Close the project by using the **Close** tool.

Starting Autodesk Revit 2019

1. Choose **Start > All Programs > Autodesk > Revit 2019 > Revit 2019** from the taskbar (for Windows 7) or double-click on the Revit 2019 icon on the desktop; the Revit interface is displayed.

Opening a New Project

1. Choose **New > Project** from the **File** menu; the **New Project** dialog box is displayed, as shown in Figure 2-7.

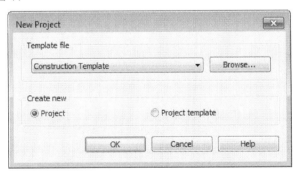

*Figure 2-7 The **New Project** dialog box*

Selecting the Template File

Before you start a Revit project, it is necessary to select a desired template file.

1. In the **New Project** dialog box, choose the **Browse** button from the **Template file** area; the **Choose Template** dialog box is displayed with a list of template files in the **US Imperial** folder. Note that for Metric system, the dialog box will display a list of template files in the **US Metric** folder.

2. In the **Choose Template** dialog box, select the **Systems-Default** template file from the list, as shown in Figure 2-8. For Metric system, select the **Systems-Default_Metric** template file from the list. Choose the **Open** button the **Choose Template** dialog box is closed.

3. Next, in the **New Project** dialog box, ensure that the **Systems-Default.rte** (for Metric system **Systems-Default_Metric.rte)** option is selected in the drop-down list located in the **Template file** area. Also, ensure that the **Project** radio button is selected in the **Create new** area. Now, choose the **OK** button; the **New Project** dialog box is closed and the *Systems-Default.rte* template file is loaded in the current file. For Metric system the *Systems-Default_Metric.rte* is loaded in the current file. Notice that the **Project Browser** now shows different levels and views that have already been created in the selected template file.

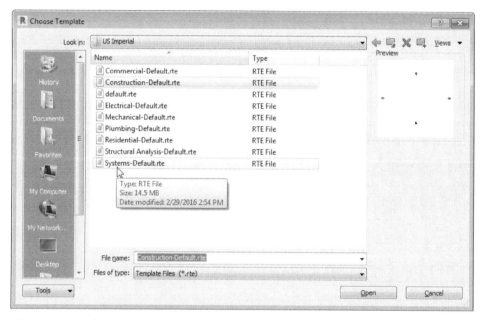

*Figure 2-8 Selecting the **Systems-Default.rte** file from the **Choose Template** dialog box*

Setting MEP Units

In this section, you will set the project units for the MEP project.

1. Choose the **Project Units** tool from the **Settings** panel of the **Manage** tab; the **Project Units** dialog box is displayed. Alternatively, you can type UN to invoke the **Project Units** dialog box.

2. In the **Project Units** dialog box, select the **HVAC** option from the **Discipline** drop-down list; various units required in the HVAC workflow are displayed in a table located below the **Discipline** drop-down list, refer to Figure 2-9.

3. Next, choose the button in the **Format** column corresponding to the **Density** parameter; the **Format** dialog box is displayed.

4. In the **Format** dialog box, select the **Pounds per cubic inch** option (for Metric system, select the **kilograms per cubic meter** option) from the **Units** drop-down list and then choose the **OK** button; the **Format** dialog box is closed.

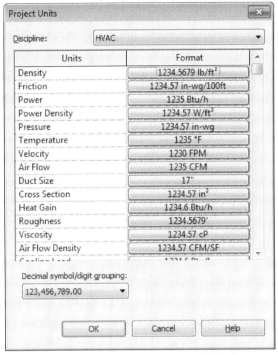

Figure 2-9 The **Project Units** dialog box

5. In the **Project Units** dialog box, repeat steps 2 to 4 and assign different units to the **Electrical**, **Piping**, and **Energy** disciplines. Refer to the table given next for the formats and the discipline of different units needed to be specified.

Discipline	Unit	Format (Imperial)	Format (Metric)
HVAC	Pressure	Pounds per square inch	Pascals
Electrical	Illuminance	Footcandles	Lux
Electrical	Apparent Power	BTU (British Thermal Units) per seconds	Watts
Piping	Density	Pounds per cubic inch	kilograms per cubic meter
Energy	Coefficient of Heat Transfer	BTU (British Thermal Units) per hour square foot degree Farenheit	Watts per square meter kelvin

6. In the **Project Units** dialog box, after specifying the various formats for different units, choose the **OK** button; the **Project Units** dialog box is closed.

Setting the Project Information

In this section, you will add the project information to the *Office-Space* project file.

1. To set the project information, choose the **Project Information** tool from the **Settings** panel of the **Manage** tab; the **Project Information** dialog box is displayed.

2. In the **Project Information** dialog box, specify the project parameters as CADSoft Technologies correspoding to the Organization Name parameter given in Figure 2-10.

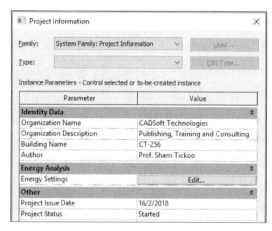

*Figure 2-10   The partial view of the **Project Information** dialog box*

3. In the **Project Information** dialog box, choose the **Edit** button displayed in the value field corresponding to the **Energy Settings** parameter; the **Energy Settings** dialog box is displayed. In this dialog box, click on the edit box corresponding to the **Mode** parameter and then select the **Use Building Elements** option from the drop-down list displayed.

4. Next, choose the **Edit** button corresponding to the **Other Options** parameter; the **Advanced Energy Settings** dialog box is displayed. In this dialog box, change the parameters as shown in the table given next and retain the other settings.

Parameter	Value
Building Type	Office
Building Operating Schedule	24/7 Facility
HVAC System	Central VAV, HW Heat, Chiller 5.96 COP, Boilers 84.5 eff
Export Category	Spaces

5. In the **Advanced Energy Settings** dialog box, choose the **OK** button; the **Energy Settings** dialog box is displayed. Choose the **OK** button in the **Energy Settings** dialog box to close

it. The specified values are assigned to the **Energy Settings** parameter in the **Project Information** dialog box.

6. In the **Project Information** dialog box, choose the **OK** button; the dialog box is closed.

Creating the Project Parameter

In this section, you will create a shared project parameter to be added to the project information.

1. Choose the **Shared Parameters** tool from the **Settings** panel of the **Manage** tab; the **Edit Shared Parameters** dialog box is displayed, refer to Figure 2-11.

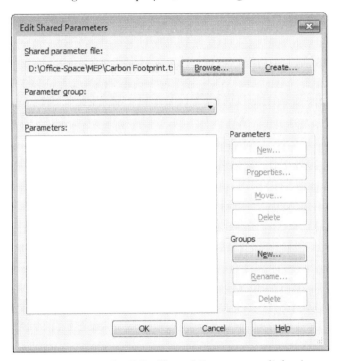

*Figure 2-11 The **Edit Shared Parameters** dialog box*

2. In the **Edit Shared Parameters** dialog box, choose the **Create** button; the **Create Shared Parameter File** dialog box is displayed.

3. In the **Create Shared Parameter File** dialog box, create a folder as per the following path *C:\Office-Space\MEP*.

4. Next, open the **MEP** folder and then enter the **Carbon Footprint** text in the **File name** edit box and then choose the **Save** button; the dialog box closes and the **Edit Shared Parameters** dialog box is displayed again.

5. In this dialog box, choose the **New** button in the **Groups** area; the **New Parameter Group** dialog box is displayed.

6. In the displayed dialog box, enter the **Green House Gas** text in the **Name** edit box and then choose the **OK** button; the **New Parameter Group** dialog box is closed and the new group is displayed in the **Parameter group** drop-down list of the **Edit Shared Parameters** dialog box.

7. Now, choose the **New** button in the **Parameters** area; the **Parameter Properties** dialog box is displayed.

8. In this dialog box, enter **Carbon Footprint Factor** in the **Name** edit box and then select the **Energy** option from the **Discipline** and **Type of Parameter** drop-down lists.

9. Now, in the **Parameter Properties** dialog box, choose the **OK** button; the dialog box is closed and the **Edit Shared Parameters** dialog box is displayed with the new parameter added.

10. In the **Edit Shared Parameters** dialog box, choose the **OK** button; the dialog box is closed.

Adding the Project Parameter to Project Information
In this section, you will add the project parameter to the project information.

1. Choose the **Project Parameters** tool from the **Settings** panel of the **Manage** tab; the **Project Parameters** dialog box is displayed.

2. In the **Project Parameters** dialog box, choose the **Add** button; the **Parameter Properties** dialog box is displayed.

3. In the **Parameter Type** area of the **Parameter Properties** dialog box, select the **Shared parameter** radio button and then choose the **Select** button; the **Shared Parameters** dialog box is displayed.

4. In this dialog box, ensure that the **Carbon Footprint Factor** parameter is selected in the **Parameters** area and then choose the **OK** button; the **Shared Parameters** dialog box is closed.

5. In the **Parameter Data** area of the **Parameter Properties** dialog box, ensure that the **Instance** and **Values are aligned per group type** radio buttons are selected. Also, ensure that the **Energy Analysis** option is selected in the **Group parameter under** drop-down list.

6. In the **Categories** area, select the **Project Information** check box from the list box displaying all categories.

7. Now, choose the **OK** button; the **Project Parameters** dialog box is displayed. Choose the **OK** button in the displayed dialog box to close it.

    After assigning the shared parameter to the category of project information, now you need to specify a value to the added parameter in the **Project Information** dialog box.

8. Choose the **Project Information** tool from the **Settings** panel of the **Manage** tab; the **Project Information** dialog box is displayed.

9. In the **Project Information** dialog box, click in the value field corresponding to the **Carbon Footprint Factor** parameter and enter **12000** in it.

10. Next, choose the **OK** button to close the **Project Information** dialog box.

Setting the Project Location

In this section, you will set the location of the project.

1. Choose the **Location** tool from the **Project Location** panel of the **Manage** tab; the **Location Weather and Site** dialog box is displayed.

2. In this dialog box, ensure that the **Location** tab is chosen by default. Now, select the **Internet Mapping Service** option from the **Define Location by** drop-down list, if it is not selected by default.

Note
*On selecting the **Internet Mapping Service** option from the **Define Location by** drop-down list, the **Google Map** browser is activated for browsing the desired location. You should ensure that the internet connection is active at this stage.*

3. In the **Location** tab of the **Location Weather and Site** dialog box, enter **Schererville, IN** in the **Project Address** edit box and then choose the **Search** button; the **Bing Map** browser is displayed under the **Project Address** edit box showing the desired location in the map, as shown in Figure 2-12.

*Figure 2-12 The **Location Weather and Site** dialog box*

4. Now, choose the **OK** button to close the **Location Weather and Site** dialog box.

Setting the Browser Organization

In this section, you will set the **Project Browser** to display various views and information related to the project in the order of their discipline.

1. Choose the **Browser Organization** tool from **View > Windows > User Interface** drop-down; the **Browser Organization** dialog box is displayed.

2. In the displayed dialog box, ensure that the **Views** tab is chosen by default and then choose the **New** button; the **Create New Browser Organization** dialog box is displayed.

3. In the **Name** edit box of the displayed dialog box, enter **Office-Space-MEP** and then choose the **OK** button; the dialog box closes and the **Browser Organization Properties** dialog box is displayed.

4. In this dialog box, choose the **Grouping and Sorting** tab; various options in this tab are displayed.

5. Select the **Discipline** option from the **Group by** drop-down list.

6. Ensure that the **All characters** radio button located under the **Group by** drop-down list is selected. Now, select the **Family and Type** option from the **Then by** drop-down list.

7. Next, select the **View Name** option from the **Sort by** drop-down list located at the bottom in the **Browser Organization Properties** dialog box. Ensure that the **Ascending** radio button located below the **Sort by** drop-down list is selected.

8. Choose the **OK** button; the **Browser Organization Properties** dialog box is closed.

9. In the **View** tab of the **Browser Organization** dialog box, select the **Office-Space-MEP** check box. Now, choose the **Apply** button and then the **OK** button; the dialog box is closed and the specified settings are applied to the **Project Browser**, refer to Figure 2-13.

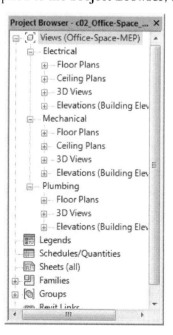

Figure 2-13 The **Project Browser** displaying the settings specified in the **Office-Space-MEP** browser organization

Saving the Project

In this section, you need to save the project and the settings using the **Save As** tool.

1. Choose **Save As > Project** from the **File** menu; the **Save As** dialog box is displayed.

2. In this dialog box, browse to the *C* drive and then create a folder with the name **rmp_2019**. Next, create a sub-folder with the name **c02_rmp_2019_tut** in it.

3. In the **File name** edit box, enter **c02_Office-Space_tut1** for Imperial or **M_c02_Office-Space_ tut1** for Metric and then choose the **Options** button; the **File Save Options** dialog box is displayed.

4. In this dialog box, enter **5** in the **Maximum backups** edit box, and then in the **Thumbnail Preview** area, select the **3D View: {3D}** option from the **Source** drop-down list.

5. Select the **Regenerate if view/sheet is not up-to-date** check box in this dialog box.

6   Now, choose the **OK** button; the **File Save Options** dialog box is closed and the **Save As** dialog box is displayed.

7. In this dialog box, choose the **Save** button to save the current project file with the specified name and to close the **Save As** dialog box.

Closing the Project

1. To close the project, choose the **Close** option from the **File** menu.

EXERCISE

Exercise 1   PowerPlant

In this exercise, you will create a new project file for the *Power Plant* project with the following parameters.   **(Expected time: 15 min)**

1. Template file:
    For Imperial   **US Imperial > Systems-Default**
    For Metric   **US Metric > Systems-Default_Metric**

2. Project information to be added:
    Project Issue Date   **10/05/2016**
    Project Status   **Started**
    Client Name   **CADSoft Technologies**
    MEP Consultant   **CADSoft Technologies**
    Mechanical Consultant   **Sham Tickoo**
    Project Name   **Power Plant**
    Commencement Date   **20/09/2016**
    Documented Contract Completion Date   **31/07/2019**
    Provisional Period Allowed in Contract   **30 Days**

3. Project Units- Set the various units in the *Power Plant* project as mentioned in the table given next.

Discipline	Units	Format (Imperial)	Format (Metric)
HVAC	Power	Kilowatts	Kilowatts
HVAC	Heat Gain	Kilowatts	Kilowatts
HVAC	Duct Size	Decimal inches	Millimeters
HVAC	Factor	Fixed	Fixed
HVAC	Pressure	Pounds per square inches	Pascals
Electrical	Frequency	Cycles per second	Cycles per second
Electrical	Current	Kiloamperes	Kiloamperes
Electrical	Illuminance	Footcandles	Lux
Electrical	Electrical Potential	Kilovolts	Kilovolts
Piping	Velocity	Feet per second	Meters per second
Energy	Coefficient of Heat Transfer	BTU per hour	Joules

4. Energy Settings-Set it as specified in the table given next.

Parameter	Value
Export Category	Spaces
Mode	Use Conceptual Masses and Building Elements
Project Phase	Existing
Building Type	Automotive Facility
Building Operating Schedule	24/7 Facility
HVAC System	Central VAV, HW Heat, Chiller 5.96 COP, Boilers 84.5 eff

5. File name to be assigned:

    For Imperial   *c02_Power_Plant_exer1.rvt*
    For Metric   *M_c02_Power_Plant_exer1.rvt*

Chapter 3

Creating Building Envelopes

Learning Objectives

After completing this chapter, you will be able to:
- *Understand the concept of Levels and Grids*
- *Understand walls*
- *Add doors and windows*
- *Create ceilings*
- *Create floors*
- *Create rooms*

INTRODUCTION

The building envelope behaves as a physical barrier between the interior and exterior of a building. It comprises of walls, floors, roofs, fenestrations and doors. In a project, fenestration are any opening in the structure such as windows, skylights, clerestories, etc. In a Revit project, the building envelope also comprises of beams, columns, datum elements, and standard views.

In an HVAC system, the building envelope is considered as an important aspect of an HVAC design. The building evelope is the outer shell that maintain a dry, heated, or cooled indoor environment and facilitate its climate control. Building envelope design is a specialized area of architectural and engineering practice that draws from all areas of building science and indoor climate control. While working in an MEP project you can either create a building envelope in the current MEP project or link the architectural and structural models created in Revit to the current MEP project.

In this chapter, you will learn about various tools and options to create the Building Envelope for carrying out an MEP project.

LEVELS

Levels, in a multistory building, refer to the infinite horizontal planes that define each story of the structure. Autodesk Revit uses levels as references for level-hosted elements such as walls, ducts, AHUs, air terminals, pipes and pipe fixtures, sanitary fixtures, floor, roof, ceiling, and so on. The distance between levels can be used to define the story height of a building model, as shown in Figure 3-1. Autodesk Revit also provides flexibility to create a non-story level or a reference level such as sill level, parapet level, and so on.

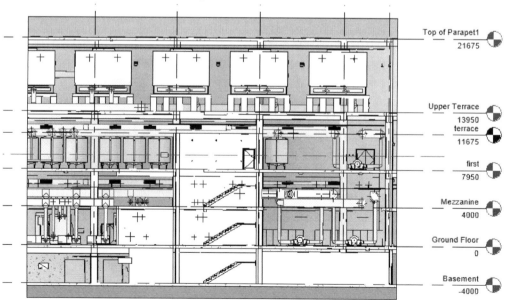

Figure 3-1 *The elevation view of a building model displaying different levels*

Adding Levels

In Autodesk Revit, you can create multiple levels based on your project requirements. Note that the **Level** tool remains inactive in the **Datum** panel for all the plan views. The **Level** tool will only be activated in an elevation or section view. To create a level, first select the desired section or elevation view on which you want to add the level. Next, invoke the **Level** tool from the **Datum** panel of the **Architecture** tab, as shown in Figure 3-2; the **Modify | Place Level** tab will be displayed. In this tab, choose any of the sketching options displayed in the **Draw** panel to create levels in your project. You can also invoke the **Level** tool by typing **LL**. In the displayed tab, you can select level type from the **Type Selector** drop-down list to modify an existing level. This drop-down list has three level types in Imperial unit system: **Level: 1/4" Head**, **Level: No Head**, and **Plenum**. In Metric unit system, the **Type Selector** drop-down list displays two types of levels: **Level: 8mm Head** and **Level: Plenum**. To make the level head visible, select the **Level: 1/4" Head** option for Imperial or **Level: 8mm Head** for Metric system. Else, select the **Level: No Head** or **Plenum** option.

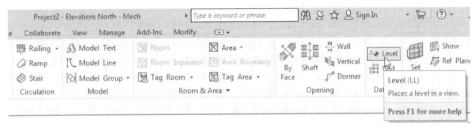

*Figure 3-2 Choosing the **Level** tool from the **Datum** panel*

WORKING WITH GRIDS

Autodesk Revit provides you the option of creating rectangular or circular grids for your projects. Using these grids, you can create building envelopes easily and also place the MEP elements at desired locations and intersections.

Creating Grids

You can create grid patterns based on your project requirement. Grid patterns can be rectangular or radial, depending on the project geometry. A rectangular grid pattern can be created using straight grid lines, whereas a radial grid pattern can be formed using arc grids. The created grids are visible in all plan, elevation, and section views.

To create a grid line, invoke the view in which you want to create it and then choose the **Grid** tool from the **Datum** panel of the **Architecture** tab, as shown in Figure 3-3; the **Modify|Place Grid** tab will be displayed. Using this tab, you can modify the type and instance properties of grid. You can also change the grid type by selecting an option from the **Type Selector** drop-down list. The **Modify | Place Grid** tab, as shown in Figure 3-4, displays various options to draw and modify grids in a drawing. The **Draw** panel in the **Modify | Place Grid** tab displays various tools to draw grids as lines and curves or to convert existing model lines into grids.

*Figure 3-3 Choosing the **Grid** tool from the **Datum** panel*

*Figure 3-4 Various options in the **Modify / Place Grid** contextual tab*

REFERENCE PLANES

Reference planes are useful while sketching and adding building elements to a design. They can be used as datum planes that act as a guideline for creating elements. They can also be used effectively for creating new family elements. To create a reference plane, choose the **Ref Plane** tool from the **Work Plane** panel of the **Architecture** tab; the **Modify | Place Reference Plane** tab will be displayed. Select the tools from the **Draw** panel and start drawing the reference plane in the drawing. Alternatively, you can type **RP** to invoke the **Ref Plane** tool.

After invoking the tool, click at the desired location in the drawing window to start a line that defines the reference plane. Now, move the cursor to the new location and release the left button to specify the endpoint of the reference line; the reference plane will be created. To assign a name to the reference plane, select it from the drawing. Next, in the **Properties** palette, enter the desired name of the selected reference plane in the value field of the **Name** instance parameter.

WORK PLANES

As the name suggests, the work plane is a plane that can be used for sketching elements. In Autodesk Revit, you can create and edit only those elements that lie in the current work plane. The work plane can be horizontal, vertical, or inclined at any specified angle. Each generated view has an associated work plane. This workplane is automatically defined for some standard views such as floor plans. For other views such as sections, elevations, and 3D views, you can set the work plane based on the location of the elements that are to be created or edited. The concept of work planes is quite useful for creating elements in elevations, sections, or inclined planes.

UNDERSTANDING WALL TYPES

Autodesk Revit provides you with several predefined wall types based on their usage. These wall types are discussed next.

Exterior Wall Type

This is the wall type that is primarily used for generating the exterior of the building model. It has predefined wall types, such as **Brick on CMU**, **Brick on Mtl. Stud**, **CMU Insulated**, and so on.

Curtain Wall Type

Apart from the above discussed wall types, Autodesk Revit also has predefined curtain walls or screen walls that consist of panels and mullions.

Autodesk Revit also provides you with the flexibility of creating your own wall type. The walls that you will create can have different functions, which can be modified, depending on their functional usage. In Autodesk Revit, you can create both architectural and structural walls. An architectural wall does not contain analytical properties as the structural walls do. In the next section, various techniques to create and modify architectural walls are discussed.

CREATING ARCHITECTURAL WALLS

In Autodesk Revit, each wall type has specific predefined properties such as composition, material, characteristics, finish, height, and so on. You can select the wall type based on its specific usage in the project. Walls, like most other model elements, can be created in a plan view or a 3D view.

To create an exterior architectural wall, first you need to invoke the **Wall: Architectural** tool and then select the appropriate exterior wall type and specify various properties. To do so, invoke the **Wall: Architectural** tool from the **Build** panel, refer to Figure 3-5; the **Modify | Place Wall** tab will be displayed. To select the type of wall, select an exterior wall type from the **Type Selector** drop-down list in the **Properties** palette. Next, from the **Properties** palette, specify and edit various properties of the wall to be added.

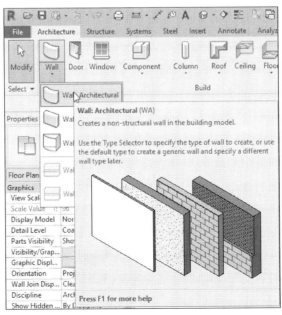

Figure 3-5 Invoking the Wall: Architectural tool from the Wall drop-down

USING DOORS IN A BUILDING MODEL

A door is one of the most frequently used components in a building model. It helps in accessing various exterior and interior spaces in a project. Autodesk Revit provides a variety of predefined door types. You can access these door types by using the options from the **Type Selector** drop-down list of the **Properties** palette. You can also load other door types from the **US Imperial** folder. A wall acts as a host element for doors. This means that a door can be placed only if there exists a wall. When you add a door to a wall, Autodesk Revit intuitively creates an opening in it.

ADDING WINDOWS IN A BUILDING MODEL

Windows form an integral part of any building project. Autodesk Revit provides several in-built window types that can be easily used and added to the building model. Like doors, windows are also dependent on the walls that act as their host element. In Autodesk Revit, the windows are not loaded in any of the default templates. To add the windows, you need to add the window families to the current file. To do so, choose the **Load Family** tool from the **Load from Library** panel of the **Insert** tab; the **Load Family** dialog box will be displayed. In this dialog box, you can browse to **US Imperial > Windows** folder for Imperial or **US Metric > Windows** folder for Metric and select the desired window type(s) from the displayed list of families. After selecting the window families, choose the **Open** button; the **Load Family** dialog box will close and the **Specify Types** dialog box will be displayed. Select the desired type(s) from the **Type** area of the dialog box. Note that you can use the CTRL key to select multiple types from the **Type** area. After selecting the desired type choose the **OK** button in the **Specify Types** dialog box and the desired window types will be added in the current project. Now, you can add the window to the building model as required.

CREATING ARCHITECTURAL FLOORS

You can add a floor to the current level of a building model using the **Floor: Architectural** tool. You can invoke this tool from the **Build** panel of the **Architecture** tab. On invoking this tool, the **Modify | Create Floor Boundary** tab will be displayed. You can use this tab to draw, annotate, and edit a floor boundary for your building model as well as to assign properties to them. The **Draw** panel of the **Modify | Create Floor Boundary** tab consists of various tools that are used to draw the floor sketches. These sketches define the boundary of the floor. To define the boundary of the floor, you can either pick the existing walls or sketch the boundary in the plan view by using lines. You can also sketch the boundary in the 3D view, provided that the work plane is set to the plan view.

PLACING CEILINGS

You can add a ceiling to a building model by using the **Ceiling** tool. To do so, invoke this tool from the **Build** panel in the **Architecture** tab; the **Modify | Place Ceiling** tab with various tools for creating the ceiling will be displayed. Since the ceilings are not visible in the floor plan, they are created in the ceiling plan head of each discipline. You can add a ceiling to a project using three different methods, by adding automatic ceiling, by sketching the ceiling, and by using the pick walls method.

CREATING ROOMS

Room is a part of Revit building elements. Revit provides you the flexibility of creating rooms independent of room tags. Rooms can be created only in the plan view. You can also add rooms from the room schedules. Rooms and areas have the same graphical representation. Also, Revit forms the basis for creating spaces.

CUTTING OPENINGS IN A WALL, FLOOR, AND CEILING

In Autodesk Revit, you can create an opening in the wall, floor, structural floor, ceiling, and structural elements such as beams and braces. To do so, invoke any of the tools from the **Opening** panel of the **Architecture** tab, as shown in Figure 3-6. From this panel, you can choose any of these five options, **By Face**, **Wall**, **Vertical**, **Shaft**, or **Dormer** to create an opening. In Revit, to create openings, you need to change the **Discipline** parameter of view to **Architecture**.

*Figure 3-6 The tools in the **Opening** panel*

Creating Openings Using the By Face Tool

You can use the **By Face** tool to create openings on the faces of floors, or ceilings in the building model. This tool is useful in a project when you need to cut an opening in a floor for stairway and in the ceiling for a chimney. To do so, invoke this tool from the **Opening** panel; you will be prompted to select a planar face of required floor, ceiling, beam, or column. Select the face on which you want to create the opening; the **Modify | Create Opening Boundary** tab will be displayed. In this tab, you can use various tools to sketch the opening in desired view. Now, open the required view and sketch the opening using the reference planes, as shown in Figure 3-7. After sketching the opening boundary on the selected face, choose the **Finish Edit Mode** button from the **Mode** panel to finish the sketch of the opening and then exit the **Modify | Create Opening Boundary** tab. Figure 3-8 shows the opening created perpendicular to the selected face.

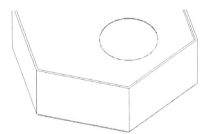
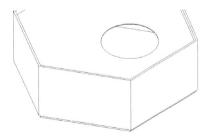

Figure 3-7 Sketching the opening in the ceiling plan using the reference planes

Figure 3-8 Opening created perpendicular to the selected face

Creating Openings Using the Vertical Tool

To cut a vertical opening, choose the **Vertical** tool from the **Opening** panel and select the required ceiling, or floor; the **Modify | Create Opening Boundary** tab will be displayed. You can use various tools from this tab to sketch the boundary of the opening. Sketch the opening in the appropriate view using the sketching tools. After sketching the opening boundary, choose the **Finish Edit Mode** button from the **Mode** panel; a vertical opening will be created in the selected element. You can use the sketching tools to draw a sketch of appropriate size, as shown in Figure 3-9. The opening can also be viewed in the 3D view, as shown in Figure 3-10.

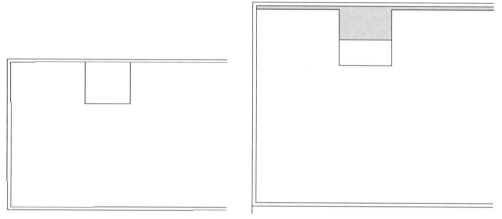

Figure 3-9 *Sketching the opening in the ceiling plan view*   *Figure 3-10* *3D view of the opening in ceiling*

Creating Openings Using the Wall Tool

To create a rectangular opening in a wall, choose the **Wall** tool from the **Opening** panel in the **MEP** tab; you will be prompted to select a wall. Select the wall in which you want to cut an opening and then sketch a rectangular opening of the required size by clicking and dragging the cursor.

Creating Openings Using the Dormer Tool

To create a dormer opening in the dormer roof, choose the **Dormer** tool from the **Opening** panel; you will be prompted to select the roof in which you want to create a dormer opening. Select the roof; the screen will enter the sketch mode. Choose the **Pick Roof/ Wall Edges** tool from the **Pick** panel of the **Modify | Edit Sketch** tab and pick the boundary of the dormer to create the dormer opening. Next, choose the **Finish Edit Mode** button from the **Mode** panel; a dormer opening will be created.

Note
The boundary that you will pick for the dormer opening in a roof should be an edge of the selected roof, wall, or both, and should form a closed loop.

Creating Openings Using the Shaft Tool

To cut an opening up to the entire height of a building, choose the **Shaft** tool from the **Opening** panel; the **Modify | Create Shaft Opening Sketch** tab will be displayed. Choose a suitable sketching tool from this tab to create an opening of the required shape. Next, choose the **Finish Edit Mode** button from the **Mode** panel; the opening will be created passing through the entire height of the building. Make sure that before sketching the opening, you select the required work plane and the view to sketch the opening.

You can also specify the levels that will be cut by the opening. It will help you to restrict the opening to a particular level. To specify the levels, select the opening; the **Modify | Shaft Openings** tab will be displayed. Select a level for the **Base Constraint** parameter in the **Properties** palette to start the opening. Next, select a level for the **Top Constraint** parameter to end the opening. The opening will be cut through the selected levels.

TUTORIALS

Tutorial 1   Office Building I

In this tutorial, you will create the exterior and interior walls, add grids, and modify levels in office building based on the sketch plan shown in Figure 3-11. The dimensions have been given only for reference and are not to be used in this tutorial. The project file and the parameters to be used for creating the walls and for adding grids and modifying levels are given next.

(Expected time: 30 min)

1. Project file-
    - For Imperial   *Systems Default*
    - For Metric   *Systems-Default_Metric*
2. Exterior Wall type-
    - For Imperial   **Generic- 9".**
    - For Metric   **Generic- 230mm.**
3. Interior Wall type-
    - For Imperial   **Generic - 5".**
    - For Metric   **Generic - 90mm.**
4. Location line parameter- **Wall Centerline**; Top Constraint- **Up to Level 2**.
5. Rename Level 1 as the Ground Floor
6. Grids to be created in the plan view.
7. File name to be assigned:
    - For Imperial   *c03_Office_BuildingI_tut1.rvt*
    - For Metric   *M_c03_Office_BuildingI_tut1.rvt*

The following steps are required to complete this tutorial:

a. Open the required template file.
    - For Imperial   *Systems Default*
    - For Metric   *Systems-Default_Metric*
b. Invoke the **Wall: Architectural** tool from the ribbon.
c. Select the required exterior wall type from the **Properties** palette.
    - For Imperial   **Generic- 9"**
    - For Metric   **Generic- 230mm**

d. Select the required interior wall type from the **Properties** palette.
       For Imperial   **Generic- 5"**
       For Metric   **Generic- 90mm**
e. Modify Top Constraint- **Up to Level: Level 2** and Location Line - **Wall Centerline** as wall properties using the **Properties** palette.
f. Invoke the **Rectangle** tool and then sketch the exterior walls based on the given parameters.
g. Sketch the interior walls based on the given parameters.
h. Modify levels by renaming them.
i. Add grids using the **Grid** tool.
j. Save and close the project.

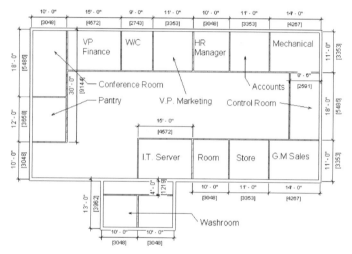

Figure 3-11 Sketch plan for creating exterior walls for the Office Building

Opening a New Project and Using the Template File

1. Choose **New > Project** from the **File** menu; the **New Project** dialog box is displayed.

2. In the **New Project** dialog box, choose the **Browse** button and then select the following template:
       For Imperial   **Systems-Default**
       For Metric   **Systems-Default_Metric**

    Next, choose the **Open** button and then the **OK** button; the desired template file is loaded. Notice that the **Project Browser** now shows several views that are preloaded in the template file.

3. In the **Project Browser**, select **1-Mech** under the **Mechanical** head, if it is not selected by default and right-click to display a flyout. From this flyout, choose **Duplicate View > Duplicate**; **1 - Mech Copy 1** is displayed under the **Mechanical** head.

4. Double click on **1 - Mech Copy 1** to display the corresponding view. Now, in the **Properties** palette, click on the value field corresponding to the **Discipline** parameter. Select the **Architectural** discipline from the drop-down list and choose the **Apply** button to apply the changes.

5. Now, the **Architectural** head is added under the **Views (Discipline)** in the **Project Browser** and under that head, **1 - Mech Copy 1** is displayed.

6. Select the **1 - Mech Copy 1** under the **Architectural Plan** head and right-click to display a flyout. From the flyout, choose the **Rename** option; the edit box is displayed. Enter **Level 1** in the edit box and choose the **OK** button; the dialog box is closed and the view is renamed to **Level 1**.

7. Repeat the procedure followed in steps 3 through 6 to duplicate another level as **Level 2** from **Mechanical** head into **Architectural** head, as shown in Figure 3-12.

8. In the **Project Browser**, select **East-Mech** under the **Mechanical** head and **Elevations** sub-head of the **Mechanical** head and right-click to display a flyout. From this flyout, choose **Duplicate View > Duplicate**; **East - Mech Copy 1** is displayed under the **Elevations** sub-head in the **Mechanical** head.

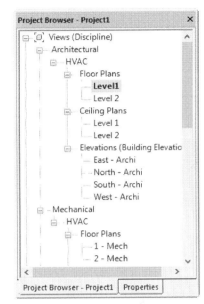

9. Double-click on **East - Mech Copy 1** to display the corresponding view. Now, in the **Properties** palette, click on the value field corresponding to the **Discipline** parameter. Select the **Architectural** discipline from the drop-down list and choose the **Apply** button to apply the change.

10. Now, in the **Project Browser** window, **East - Mech Copy 1** is displayed under the **Views (Discipline) > Architectural > Elevations (Building Elevation)**.

*Figure 3-12 The **Properties** Palette displaying other views under the **Elevations** sub-head*

11. Select **East - Mech Copy 1** under the **Architectural Plan** head and right-click to display a flyout. From the flyout, choose the **Rename** option; the edit box is displayed. Enter **East - Archi** in the edit box and choose the **OK** button; the dialog box is closed and the view is renamed to **East - Archi**.

12. Repeat the procedure followed in steps 8 through 10 to add other views under the **Elevations** sub-head, refer to Figure 3-12.

Invoking the Wall: Architectural Tool and Selecting the Wall Type

In this section, you will sketch an architectural wall using the **Wall** tool.

1. Double-click on the **Level 1** view under the **Views (Discipline) > Architectural > HVAC > Floor Plans**; the corresponding view is displayed.

2. Invoke the **Wall: Architectural** tool from the **Architecture > Build > Wall** drop-down; the **Modify | Place Wall** tab is displayed.

3. In the **Type Selector** drop-down list of the **Properties** palette, select the **Generic - 8"** wall type for Imperial or **Generic - 200mm** wall type for Metric unit system.

4. In the **Properties** palette, choose the **Edit Type** button; the **Type Properties** dialog box is displayed.

5. Choose the **Duplicate** button from the upper right corner of this dialog box; the **Name** dialog box is displayed. Enter **Generic- 9"** for Imperial (**Generic- 230mm** for Metric system) in the **Name** edit box and then choose the **OK** button; the dialog box is closed and the **Generic - 9"** for Imperial system (**Generic - 230mm** for Metric system) is selected in the **Type** drop-down list.

6. Now, choose the **Edit** button from the value field corresponding to the **Structure** parameter; the **Edit Assembly** dialog box is displayed.

7. In the **Edit Assembly** dialog box, click on the value field of the **Thickness** column corresponding to the **Structure[1]** function parameter. Enter **9"** for Imperial or enter **230mm** for Metric and then choose the **OK** button; the **Edit Assembly** dialog box is closed.

8. Now, choose **OK** button; the **Type Properties** dialog box is closed and the **Generic - 9"** wall type is selected in Imperial system or **Generic - 230mm** is selected in the **Type Selector** drop-down list.

Modifying the Properties of the Exterior Wall

After sketching the wall type, you need to modify the instance properties of the wall type using the **Properties** palette.

1. In the **Properties** palette, ensure that the **Location Line** parameter has **Wall Centerline** as the default value. Click in the value field of the **Top Constraint** instance parameter; a drop-down list is displayed. Select **Up to Level: Level 2** from the drop-down list displayed, as shown in Figure 3-13 and choose the **Apply** button.

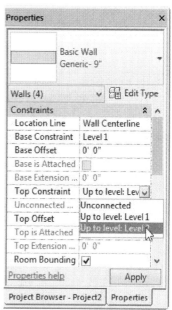

*Figure 3-13 Setting the **Top Constraint** parameter using the **Properties** palette*

Sketching the Exterior Wall Segment

In this section, you will sketch the exterior wall segment.

1. Invoke the **Rectangle** tool from the **Draw** panel of the **Modify | Place Wall** tab.

2. Click between the four elevation symbols in the drawing area to specify the first point. Next, move the cursor toward bottom right to draw a rectangle. On doing so, a rectangle starts creating from a specified point. Now, click to specify the endpoint, as shown in Figure 3-14.

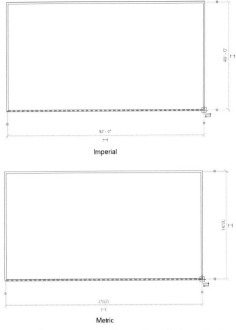

Figure 3-14 *The temporary dimensions being displayed on the sketched wall*

3. Click on the temporary dimension of the horizontal wall displayed; an edit box appears showing the current dimension of the wall segment.

4. Enter **80'** for Imperial or **24000 mm** for Metric in the edit box and then press ENTER; the length of the horizontal wall is modified to the entered value.

5. Similarly, click on the temporary dimension of vertical wall; an edit box appears. Enter **40'** for Imperial or **12000 mm** for Metric in the edit box and then press ENTER; the length of the vertical wall is modified to the entered value. Press ESC twice to exit the **Modify | Walls** tab.

The external wall profile is drawn with the specified dimensions, as shown in Figure 3-15.

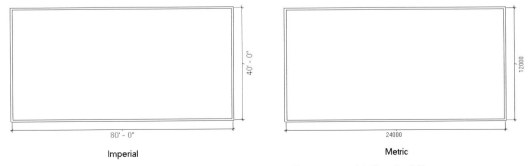

Figure 3-15 *The completed exterior wall segment of Office Building*

Sketching Other Exterior Wall Segments

In this section, you need to create other exterior wall segments.

1. Choose the **Wall: Architectural** tool from the **Architecture > Build > Wall** drop-down; the **Modify | Place Wall** tab is displayed.

2. Choose the **Line** tool from the **Draw** panel of the **Modify | Place Wall** tab. Ensure that the **Chain** check box is selected in the **Options Bar**. Now, place the cursor to the lower left corner of the wall and move toward right. When temporary dimension appears, enter **20'** for Imperial or enter **6000 mm** for Metric and then press ENTER.

3. Draw **13'0"** line in Imperial system or **3900 mm** line in Metric system from that point in downward direction, as shown in Figure 3-16.

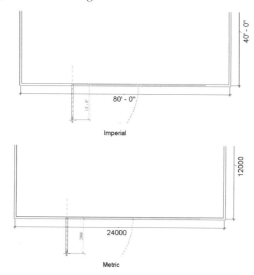

Figure 3-16 *The other exterior wall segment created outside the Office Building*

4. After drawing the line, the wall starts creating dynamically with one end attached to the specified point and the other end attached to the cursor. Move the cursor horizontally toward the right so that you see a dashed horizontal line inside the wall segment. Now, enter **20'0"** for Imperial or **6000 mm** for Metric as the value of the length; an edit box is displayed with the dimension you have entered, as shown in Figure 3-17.

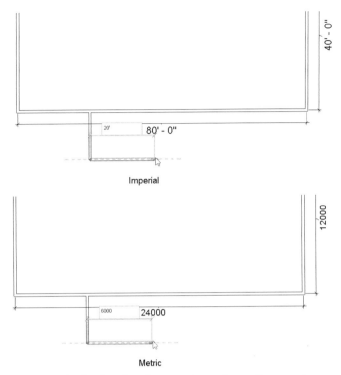

Figure 3-17 *Creating the second exterior wall segment*

5. Now you need to draw the third wall segment. To do so, move the cursor upward and enter **13'** for Imperial or enter **3900 mm** for Metric as the value of the length and press ENTER. The other exterior wall segments are created, as shown in Figure 3-18.

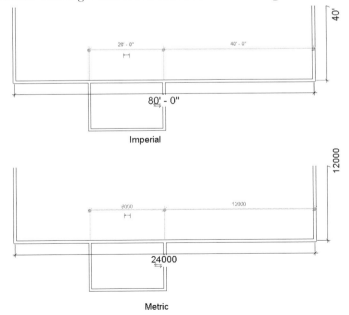

Figure 3-18 *The completed exterior profile of Office Building*

6.   Now, press ESC or choose the **Modify** button to clear the selection.

Selecting the Interior Wall Type

In this section, you will select the interior wall type.

1.   Invoke the **Wall: Architectural** tool; the wall instance parameters are displayed in the **Properties** palette. In this palette, select the required wall type from the **Type Selector** drop-down list, as shown in Figure 3-19.

     For Imperial   **BasicWall Generic - 5"**
     For Metric   **BasicWall Generic - 90mm**

2.   In the **Options Bar**, select the **Wall Centerline** option from the **Location Line** drop-down list, if it is not selected by default.

Sketching Other Interior Walls

Next, you will sketch other horizontal or vertical interior walls by specifying their start point and end point using different object snap options.

1.   Move the cursor near the top left end of the wall and then start moving the cursor horizontally toward the right. Enter **10'0"** for Imperial or **3000 mm** for Metric when the temporary dimensions and the intersection object snap appear, as shown in Figure 3-20. Now, press ENTER; the starting point of the first interior wall is specified.

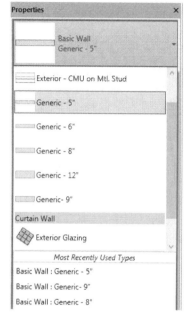

Figure 3-19 Selecting the interior wall type from the ***Type Selector*** *drop-down list*

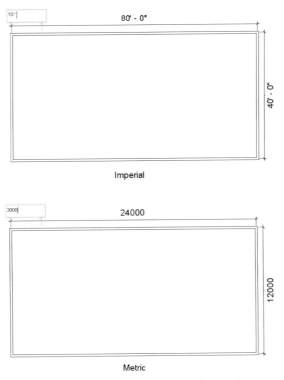

Figure 3-20 *Specifying the distance for starting the first interior wall segment*

2. Next, move the cursor vertically downward and enter **30'** for Imperial (**9000 mm** for Metric) and close the wall segment, as shown in Figure 3-21; the interior wall segment is sketched.

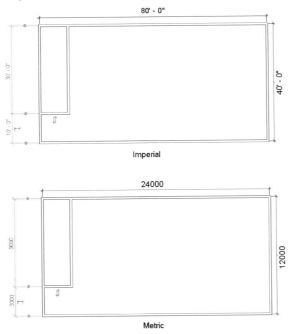

Figure 3-21 *Specifying the first interior wall segment*

3. To sketch the second interior wall, move the cursor to the upper endpoint of the interior wall you just created and then move the cursor vertically downward. Enter 11'0" for Imperial or 3300 mm for Metric when the temporary dimension and the intersection object snap appears as shown in Figure 3-22.

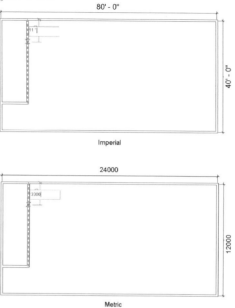

Figure 3-22 *Specifying the starting point of second interior wall segment*

4. Press SHIFT and move the cursor toward right near the right exterior wall segment. Now, click to specify the location of the endpoint of the wall segment; the second interior wall segment is sketched, as shown in Figure 3-23

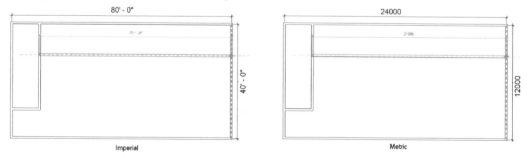

Figure 3-23 *Sketching the second interior wall*

5. To sketch the third interior wall, place the cursor toward the lower right corner of the wall segment and move the cursor upward. Enter **11'0"** for Imperial or **3300** mm for Metric and then press ENTER, as shown in Figure 3-24; the starting point of the interior wall is specified.

6. Next, move the cursor in a horizontal direction toward the left. Enter **50'0"** for Imperial and **15000** for Metric and then press ENTER, as shown in Figure 3-25. Ensure that the **Chain** option is selected. Now, move the cursor vertically downward near the lower exterior wall segment; the interior wall segment is sketched, as shown in Figure 3-26.

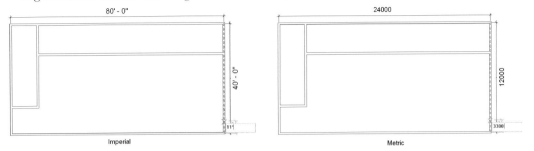

Figure 3-24 *Specifying the distance for starting the first interior wall segment*

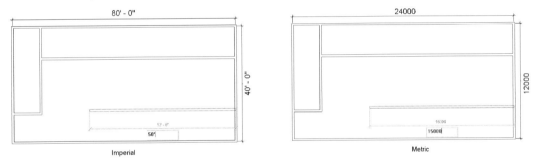

Figure 3-25 *Specifying the distance for starting the interior wall segment*

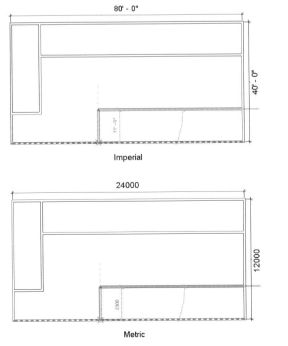

Figure 3-26 *Sketched wall segment*

7.   Similarly, you can draw other interior walls by using the **Line** tool, refer to Figure 3-27.

8.   Choose the **Modify** button to exit the tool.

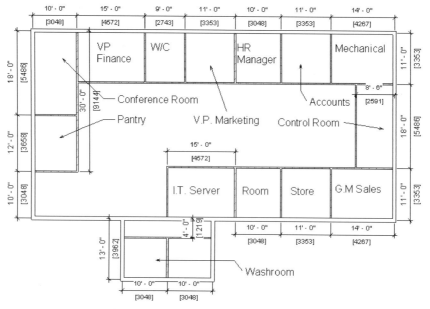

Figure 3-27 Layout of internal walls for Office Building

Modifying Levels

In this section, you will invoke the **Level** tool in the elevation view.

1.   In the **Project Browser**, double-click on the **North - Archi** under the **Elevations (Building Elevation)** head; the north elevation is displayed within the existing levels in the drawing window.

2.   Choose the **Zoom in Region** tool from the Navigation Bar to enlarge the right portion of the elevation showing the levels, refer to Figure 3-28.

3.   To rename the levels, move the cursor over **Level 1** in the **Project Browser** and right-click; a shortcut menu is displayed.

4.   Choose the **Rename** option from the shortcut menu; the edit box is displayed.

5.   In the displayed edit box, enter **Ground Floor** and choose the **OK** button; you are prompted to verify whether you want to rename the corresponding levels and views.

6.   Choose the **Yes** button to rename the level and views. The level is immediately renamed in the elevation view.

7.   Similarly, rename the **Level 2** as **Roof** , as shown in Figure 3-28.

Figure 3-28 *Renamed levels and views for the Office Building*

Creating Grid Lines

You can use the plan view to add grids to the project using the **Grid** tool. Grids are automatically numbered as they are created. Now, you will create Grids in the sequence as shown in the sketch plan.

1. Double-click on **Ground Floor** from the **Floor Plans** head in the **Project Browser** to display the ground floor plan in the drawing window.

2. Next, choose the **Grid** tool from the **Datum** panel of the **Architecture** tab; the **Modify | Place Grid** tab is displayed.

3. Now, ensure that the **Line** tool is chosen in the **Draw** panel.

4. Move the cursor near the top left corner of the exterior wall profile till a vertical extension line is displayed. Click to specify the start point of the grid line when the temporary dimension of **3'0"** for Imperial or **900 mm** for metric is displayed from the centerline of the exterior wall, as shown in Figure 3-29.

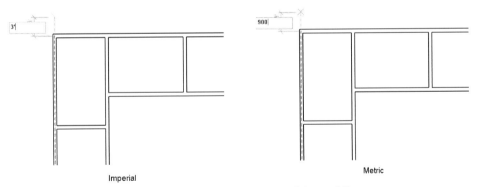

Imperial   Metric

Figure 3-29 *Specifying the start point of the grid line*

5. Move the cursor vertically downward and click outside the south wall to specify the endpoint of the grid line, as shown in Figure 3-30.

Note
*If grid lines are not visible in the drawing, choose the **Visibility/Graphics** tool from the **Graphics** panel of the **View** tab to display the **Visibility/Graphic Overrides for Floor Plan** dialog box. In the **Annotation Categories** tab of this dialog box, select the **Grids** check box; the grid lines will become visible.*

The same procedure can be followed to draw grid lines for the interior walls. As the thickness of the interior wall is 5" or 90 mm, you can specify 2 1/2" or 64 mm as the offset distance to draw grid lines for the interior walls.

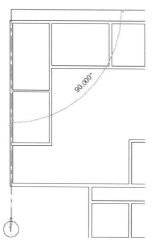

Figure 3-30 *Specifying the grid line drawn at first point*

6. Repeat steps 3, 4, and 5 to create other vertical and horizontal grid lines in the sequence of their numbers using the **Pick Line** tool. After adding grid lines, press ESC twice to exit. Figure 3-31 shows the floor plan after adding grid lines.

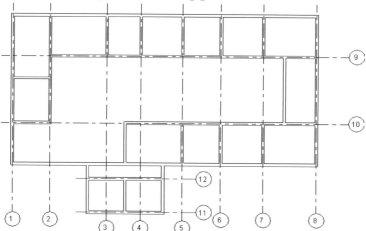

Figure 3-31 *The horizontal and vertical grid lines created for wall centerline*

Note

*You can rename a grid by selecting it from the drawing and then entering a value corresponding to the value column for the **Name** parameter in the **Properties** palette. The entered value will be the new name of the grid.*

This completes the tutorial for creating walls, adding grids, and modifying levels of the building envelope project.

Saving the Project

In this section, you need to save the project and the settings using the **Save As** tool.

1. Choose **Save As > Project** from the **File** menu; the **Save As** dialog box is displayed.

2. In this dialog box, browse to *C:\rmp_2019\c03_rmp_2019_tut* and then enter **c03_Office_BuildingI_tut1** for Imperial or **M_c03_Office_BuildingI_tut1** for Metric in the **File Name** edit box.

3. Now, choose the **Save** button; the **Save As** dialog box closes and the project file is saved**.**

Closing the Project

1. Choose the **Close** option from **File** menu**.**

EXERCISE

Exercise 1   Residential Building

Create the exterior and interior walls of a residential building and then add doors and windows to them. Create floor and ceiling and then add grids to the walls of the Residential building, refer to Figure 3-32. Do not add dimensions or texts as they are given only for reference. Figure 3-33 shows the three dimensional view of the residential building with the added floors and ceilings. The project parameters for this exercise are given next.

(Expected time: 1 Hour)

1. Project File -
   For Imperial   **Systems-Default**.
   For Metric   **Systems-Default_Metric**.

2. Discipline - **Architectural**.

3. Rename Level 1 - First Floor, Level 2 - Second Floor.

4. Exterior wall type -
   For Imperial   **Basic Wall - Exterior Brick on Mtl. Stud**.
   For Metric   **Basic Wall - Exterior Brick on Mtl. Stud**.

5. Interior wall type -
   For Imperial   **Basic Wall: Generic- 5"**.
   For Metric   **Basic Wall: Generic- 90 mm**.

6. Height of wall - **Top Constraint - Upto Level 2**.

7. Door type to be used:

    For Imperial   Main door - **Double - Glass 2 - 36" x 84"**

                         Bedroom doors - **Single - Flush 30" x 84"**

                         Washroom door - **Single Flush Vision - 36" x 84"**

    For Metric   Main door - **Double - Glass 2 - 1830 x 1981mm**

                         Bedroom doors - **Single - Flush 0762 x 2134mm**

                         Washroom door - **Single Flush Vision - 0915 x 2134 mm**

8. Window type to be used:

    For Imperial   **Fixed with Trim - 36" x 24"**

    For Metric   **Fixed with Trim - 0915 x 0610 mm**

9. Floor type -

    For Imperial   **Floor: Generic- 12".**

    For Metric   **Floor: Generic- 300mm**

10. Ceiling type - **Generic**.

11. File name to be assigned:

    For Imperial   *c03_Residential-Building_exer1.rvt*

    For Metric   *M_c03_Residential-Building_exer1.rvt*

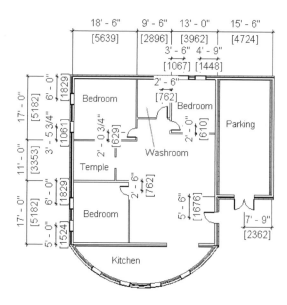

Figure 3-32   Sketch plan of walls with doors and windows, and floor and ceiling added to the building

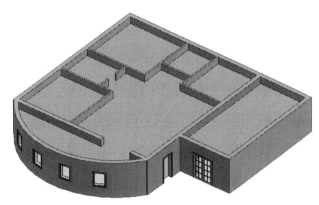

Figure 3-33 *Three dimensional view of residential building with added floors and ceilings*

This page is intenionally left blank

Chapter 4

Creating Spaces and Zones and Performing Load Analysis

After completing this chapter, you will be able to:
- *Create Spaces*
- *Modify Spaces*
- *Create Zones*
- *Modify Zones*
- *Perform Heating and Cooling Load Analysis*

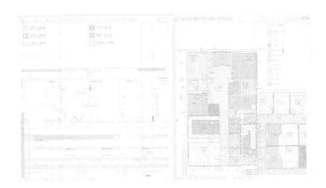

INTRODUCTION

In Autodesk Revit, you can model the spaces and create zones to efficiently track the building design and construction changes within a project file. In Revit, you can assign the HVAC load to the spaces in the model and export the space load data via a gbXML file to an external simulation software program.

While designing HVAC systems, modeling the building space accurately is one of the key criteria for correct designing. During the mechanical designing of a project, most of the time is spent on modeling the building correctly in a load-simulating program, such as Trane TRACE 700 or Carriers Hourly Analysis Program (HAP). Although these programs are essential for mechanical designer, setting up the building accurately using these programs can be a tedious task.

In an MEP model, each space is set up individually and the physical construction and the usage of each space is also different. Alterations to the building design or space usage by the architect during this phase will require returning to previously modeled spaces and modifying them. This is time-consuming and can often be a point of conflict, when changes occur later in the design phase.

In this chapter, you will learn the process of preparing the space model and create zones for analysis. Also, you will learn how to perform the heating and cooling analysis in Revit 2019. Further, you will learn how to export the gbXML data to a load-simulating software.

SPACE MODELING FOR BUILDING ANALYSIS

Modeling spaces accurately and efficiently in a building model is necessary for successful load analysis. In Revit, various components of a building have to be modeled for each space, as each component plays a vital role in building load analysis. The components that are to be modeled include building construction component, internal load component, and external load factors. These components should be considered for each space that is being created. Note that each of these components has several significant inputs that can affect the loads within the space.

Creating Spaces

You need to create spaces in a building model to perform a load analysis. In Revit, spaces are created from room bounding elements such as walls, floors, ceilings, and roofs, and from room separation lines. After creating the initial set-up for the MEP project and linking the desired architectural model in the project or creating the building envelope, the architectural elements that make up a room define your space accurately.

Figure 4-1 shows a linked architectural model. Select the linked model from the drawing area; the properties of the linked model will be displayed in the **Properties** palette. In the palette, choose the **Edit Type** button; the **Type Properties** dialog box will be displayed. In this dialog box, select the check box corresponding to the **Room Bounding** parameter; the spaces in the linked model will be bounded by room. Now, choose **OK** and **Apply** to close the **Type Properties** dialog box.

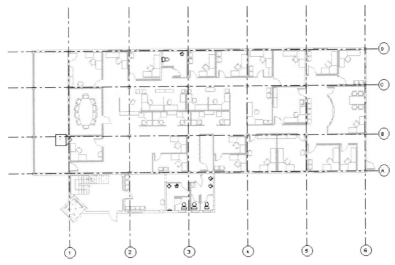

Figure 4-1 *The linked architectural model*

 Note
*In the **Type Properties** dialog box for the linked model, if you clear the check box and place a space in the model, the **Warning** message box will be displayed informing you that the created space will not be in an enclosed region, and subsequently, Revit will not be able to calculate load data for that space if HVAC analysis is attempted on the model.*

COLOR SCHEMES

Color schemes, as shown in Figure 4-2, are used to represent and categorize different spaces in the project graphically by using color codes. In other words, color schemes are used to color the spaces, rooms, and areas in a view. You can create color schemes and then apply them to different plan views. You can create different color schemes for the first and second floors of a building. A color scheme can be created based on specific categories such as gross area, rentable area, or an instance property of the space such as room cavity ratio, calculated cooling load, space type, area per person, perimeter, number, name, and more. You can also create a color scheme depending on the utilization of different spaces in a building. For example, you can assign different colors to represent areas such as office, storage, or accounts. Then, you can add a color scheme legend to help you identify different areas by the colors assigned to them. To create a color scheme for spaces, first you need to create and edit different color schemes using the **Edit Color Scheme** dialog box and then apply a scheme to the project view.

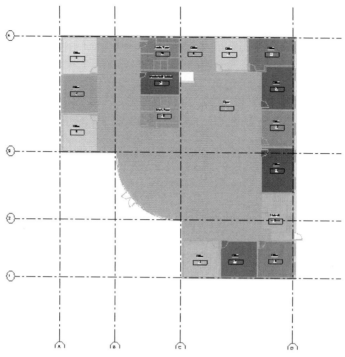

Figure 4-2 *The color scheme of spaces categorized by its assigned number*

CREATING ZONES FROM SPACES

In an MEP project, spaces that have common environmental and design requirements are grouped to form zones. Zones are formed in order to provide control on the quality or condition of similar spaces. These conditions refer to the temperature, humidity, and other information factors. By creating zones in a building, you can control the airflow to a given group of spaces, depending on the changes in the design specifications. For example, you can shut off the airflow to an area that is not occupied or increase the airflow to spaces when the changes in the space load increases.

In a zone, you can add both occupied and unoccupied areas. You can also add spaces to different levels of the same zone. You can create a zone schedule and use it to modify the zones. Every zone contains zone information, such as heating and cooling temperatures and outdoor air information. Revit uses both zone and space information during heating and cooling loads analysis to determine the energy demands of the building. The zone properties collects information from various spaces in it. The information can be the heating and cooling temperature set points alongwith other space properties. It is used with a heating and cooling loads analysis to determine the energy demands of the building.

In Revit, all projects have one zone namely the **Default** zone. All spaces in Revit are initially placed in this zone. You can also create an unbounded zone in the **Default** zone. These zones have no spaces assigned to them. You can create zones in order to satisfy the environmental requirements for areas in a project, and add spaces later. Unbounded zones can be created for design purposes, fire protection zones, and retaining information. Unbounded zones retain zone properties that you specify, and you can move (drag) them within a view for design purposes. Only unbounded zones can be moved. After a space is assigned (added) to a zone, the zone is bounded by the space(s) assigned to it, and the zone cannot be moved. Unlike a space, an unbounded zone will not snap to a bounded area. In the next sections, you will learn how to create and modify a HVAC zone in a Revit project.

PERFORMING HEATING AND COOLING LOAD ANALYSIS

In a project, after defining the spaces and assigning them to zones, you may need to perform a detailed heating and cooling load analysis. The report generated from the analysis will help you to know how sustainable will be the building throughout the project. You can use the data from the report to design the HVAC system in the building for which the analysis has been made.

To perform the heating and cooling loads analysis, choose the **Heating and Cooling Loads** tool from the **Reports & Schedules** panel of the **Analyze** tab; the **Heating and Cooling Loads** dialog box will be displayed, as shown in Figure 4-3.

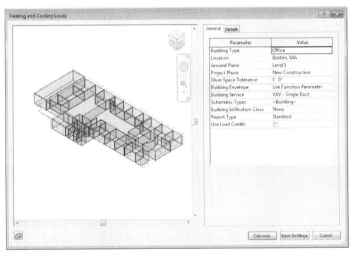

*Figure 4-3 The **Heating and Cooling Loads** dialog box displaying the options in the **General** tab*

TUTORIALS

General instructions for downloading tutorial files:

1. Download the *c04_rmp_2019_tut.zip* file for this tutorial from *http://www.cadsofttech.com*. The path of the file is as follows: *Textbooks > Civil/GIS > Revit MEP > Revit MEP 2019 for Novices*.

2. Now, save and extract the downloaded folder at the following location:
    C:\rmp_2019

Tutorial 1   Placing Spaces- Office Space

In this tutorial, you will open a linked architectural model and then add spaces to it.

(Expected time: 1 hr 15 min)

1. Template file:
    For Imperial: **US Imperial > Systems-Default**.
    For Metric: **US Metric > Systems-Default_Metric**

2. File name to be used:
    For Imperial: *c04_archi_spaces_rmp2019.rvt*
    For Metric: *M_c04_archi_spaces_rmp2019.rvt*

3. File name to be assigned:
    For Imperial: *c04_Office-Space_tut1.rvt*
    For Metric: *M_c04_Office-Space_tut1.rvt*

The following steps are required to complete this tutorial:

a. Start a Revit 2019 session.
b. Open a new project and link an architectural model.
c. Add a Plenum level.
d. Rename and modify the Plenum level.
e. Place spaces in the 1-Mech view.
f. Rename and renumber the spaces.
g. Enable the space visibility.
h. Place space in the separated area.
i. Place space in the Chase area.
j. Save the project using the **Save As** tool.
k. Close the project using the **Close** tool.

Starting Autodesk Revit 2019

1. Choose **Start > All Programs > Autodesk > Revit 2019 > Revit 2019 (for Windows 7)**;
    the Revit interface window is displayed.

Opening a New Project and Linking the Architectural Model

In this section, you will open a new project and link the downloaded .rvt file to it.

1. Choose **New > Project** from the **File** menu; the **New Project** dialog box is displayed.

2. In the **New Project** dialog box, choose the **Browse** button; the **Choose Template** file
    dialog box is displayed. In this dialog box, select the *Systems-Default.rte* (for Metric *Systems-Default_Metric.rte*) from the **US Imperial** folder (for Metric **US Metric folder**) and choose
    OK; the **Choose Template** dialog box is closed and the selected template is loaded in the
    file.

3. Now, in the **New Project** dialog box, select the **Systems Template** (for Metric **Systems-Default_Metric**) from the **Template** file drop-down list and then choose the **OK** button; the **New Project** dialog box is closed and the new project is opened.

   In the new project file, you will download the architectural model in the current project view and then link the architectural model in the **1-Mech** view under the **Mechanical > HVAC > Floor Plans** view displayed in the **Project Browser**.

4. In the **Project Browser**, ensure that the **1-Mech** node is selected under **Mechanical > HVAC > Floor Plans** and then choose the **Link Revit** tool from the **Link** panel of the **Insert** tab; the **Import/Link RVT** dialog box is displayed. In this dialog box, browse to the *C:\rmp_2019\ c04_rmp_2019_tut* folder and then select the *c04_archi_spaces_rmp2019.rvt* file. For Metric select the *M_c04_archi_spaces_rmp2019.rvt* file.

5. Now, choose the **Open** button; the selected file is linked to the current project and is displayed in the project view, as shown in Figure 4-4.

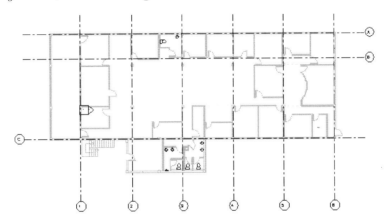

Figure 4-4 *The drawing view with the linked model*

6. Now, move the cursor over the linked model and click when a blue border is displayed around it; the **Modify|RVT Links** contextual tab is displayed.

7. In this tab, choose the **Type Properties** tool from the **Properties** panel; the **Type Properties** dialog box is displayed.

8. In this dialog box, select the check box displayed in the **Value** field corresponding to the **Room Bounding** parameter. The architectural components (such as walls and floors) are closed so that they are recognized as boundaries for spaces.

Note
While working with a linked file, make sure that the roof is defined as room bounding element and the ceiling is defined as a non-room bounding element. These components are defined in the architectural model file and not in the MEP model file.

9. In the **Type Properties** dialog box, choose the **OK** button to close it. Now, in the **Modify |
   RVT Links** contextual tab, choose the **Modify** button in the **Select** panel; the linking process
   of the architectural model is now complete.

Adding a Plenum Level

In this section, you will create a plenum level for the spaces. The plenum levels are created to
place spaces in the plenum areas (between the ceiling and the floor) of the building. You must
place spaces in all areas (occupied and unoccupied) of the building to achieve an accurate
heating and cooling load analysis.

1. In the **Project Browser**, expand **Mechanical> HVAC> Elevations (Building Elevation)**,
   and double-click in the **East - Mech** node; the east elevation view is opened.

2. Choose the **Level** tool from the **Datum** panel of the **Architecture** tab; the **Modify |Place
   Level** tab is displayed along with various options in the **Options Bar**.

3. In the **Properties** palette, select the **Level Plenum** option from the **Type Selector** drop-down
   list.

4. In the **Options Bar**, ensure that the **Make Plan View** check box is selected and then choose
   the **Plan View Types** button; the **Plan View Types** dialog box is displayed, as shown in
   Figure 4-5. In this dialog box, you will notice that the **Ceiling Plan**, **Structural Plan,** and
   Floor Plan options are selected and highlighted in the **Select view types to create** list box.

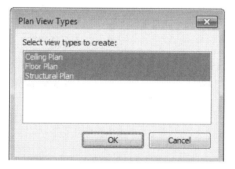

*Figure 4-5 The **Ceiling Plan**, **Structural Plan** and the **Floor Plan** options selected
in the **Plan View Types** dialog box*

5. In the list box, click on the **Structural Plan** and **Ceiling Plan** options to clear the selection
   and then choose the **OK** button; the **Plan View Types** dialog box is closed.

6. Now, in the **Draw** panel of the **Modify | Place Level** contextual tab, ensure that the **Line**
   tool is chosen and then move and place the cursor near the endpoint of **Level 1** level. Move
   the cursor up. On doing so, you will notice a temporary dimension emerging from the left
   endpoint of the **Level 1**, as shown in Figure 4-6.

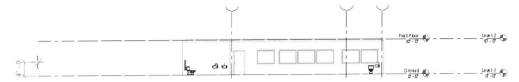

Figure 4-6 *The temporary dimension emerging from the **Level 1** line*

7. Now, type **8'6" (2591mm)** and press ENTER; the level starts at a distance of 8'6" (2591mm) from the **Level 1** level.

8. Now, move the cursor toward right and place it over the endpoint of **Level 1**. Click when the extension snap appears along with an alignment line emerging from **Level 1** line; the plenum level is created.

9. In the **Modify | Place Level** tab, choose the **Modify** button from the **Select** panel to exit the **Level** tool.

10. In the **Project Browser**, double-click on the **Mechanical 3** (for Metric **Level 3**) node in **Mechanical > HVAC > Floor Plans** node; the floor plan view of the **Mechanical 3** level is displayed in the drawing window.

Renaming and Modifying the Plenum Level

1. In the **Properties** palette, click on the value field corresponding to the **View Name** parameter and enter **1-Mech-Plenum** in the edit box to replace the existing name. Press ENTER; the **Revit** message box is displayed. Choose the **Yes** button in the displayed message box; the level is renamed.

2. In the **Properties** palette, choose the **Mechanical Plan** button displayed in the value field corresponding to the **View Template** parameter; the **Apply View Template** dialog box is displayed.

3. In the dialog box, select the **<None>** option from the **Names** list box and then choose the **OK** button; the **Apply View Template** dialog box is closed.

4. In the **Properties** palette, choose the **Edit** button displayed in the value field corresponding to the **View Range** parameter; the **View Range** dialog box is displayed.

5. In the **Primary Range** area of the dialog box, select the **Level Above (Level 2)** option from the **Top** drop-down list. Also, select the **Associated Level (1-Mech-Plenum)** option from the **Bottom** drop-down list. Now, click in the **Offset** edit box displayed next to the **Cut plane** drop-down list and enter **1' (304mm)** to replace the existing value.

6. In the **View Depth** area of the **View Range** dialog box, select the **Associated Level (1-Mech-Plenum)** option from the **Level** drop-down list. Choose **Apply** and then **OK**; the **View Range** dialog box is closed.

7. In the **Project Browser**, under **HVAC > Floor Plans**, double-click on **1 - Mech** and maximize the window. Now, choose the **Close Inactive** tool from the **Windows** panel of the **View** tab

to close the displayed elevation view. Alternatively, you can choose the **1-Mech** tab in the user interface to activate the view.

 Note
*If the active window is in the tile mode, then the **Close Inactive** tool is disabled. If more than one window is opened in the current session, choose the **Tile View** tool to tile the windows displayed.*

Placing Spaces in the 1-Mech View

In this section, you will place the spaces in the **1-Mech** floor plan view.

1. Choose the **Space** tool from the **Spaces & Zones** panel of the **Analyze** tab; the **Modify|Place Space** tab is displayed.

2. In the **Tag** panel of this tab, make sure that the **Tag on Placement** button is chosen by default. In the **Options Bar**, select the **1-Mech-Plenum** option from the **Upper Limit** drop-down list.

   In the **Options Bar**, ensure that the **0'0''** (**0.0**) value is specified in the **Offset** edit box, the **Horizontal** option is selected in the drop-down list displayed next to the **Offset** edit box, the **Leader** check box is cleared and the **New** option is selected in the **Space** drop-down list.

3. In the drawing area, zoom into the office area located in the upper-left corner of the building. Now, place the cursor in it, until the space snaps to the room-bounding elements, as shown in Figure 4-7. Click when the room bounding is highlighted; the new space is placed with the default name **Space** and number **1**.

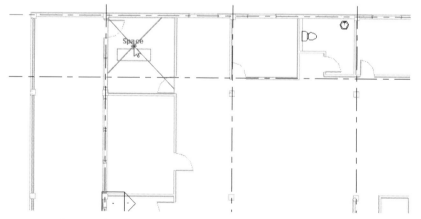

Figure 4-7 Placing the space inside the room-bounding area

4. Ensure that the **Space** tool is invoked. Then, press ZF; the project view is zoomed to fit the drawing area. This displays the entire floor plan placed at the center of the drawing area.

Tip
*You can right-click in the drawing window and select the **Zoom to Fit** option from the shortcut menu displayed*

5. Now, move the cursor to the large open area at the center of the floor plan, and after the space snaps to the room bounding elements, click to place a space, as shown in Figure 4-8.

   Make sure that you have placed the space tag toward right in the open space. Later in the tutorial, you will separate the open space near the entrance and place a space there.

6. In the **Modify | Place Space** contextual tab, choose the **Modify** button from the **Select** panel; the **Space** tool is exited.

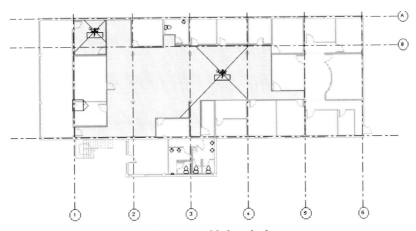

Figure 4-8 The space added to the large open area

Renaming and Renumbering the Spaces
In this section, you will rename and renumber the spaces added.

1. Zoom in the space tag in the office area in the upper-left corner and then click on the **Space** text; an edit box is displayed. Enter **CEO-Office** in the edit box and press ENTER; the space name is changed.

2. Now, in the same space, double- click on the text **1**; an edit box is displayed. Enter **101** to replace the previous number and press ENTER; the space number is changed.

3. Repeat steps 1 and 2 and rename and renumber the space at the central area as **Central Area** and **110**, respectively, refer to Figure 4-9.

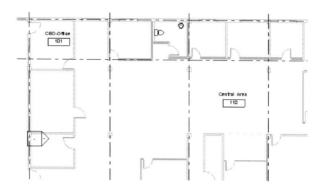

Figure 4-9 *The central area space renamed and renumbered*

Enabling the Space Visibility

In this section, you will enable the visibility of the space interior fills and markers.

1. Ensure that the **1-Mech** floor plan view is active and then choose the **Visibility/Graphics** tool from the **Graphics** panel of the **View** tab; the **Visibility/Graphics Override for Floor Plan: 1-Mech** dialog box is displayed.

2. In the dialog box, ensure that the **Model Categories** tab is chosen by default, and then in the **Visibility** column, expand the **Spaces** node. Ensure that the check box corresponding to the **Spaces** node is selected.

3. Now, under the **Spaces** node, ensure that the **Color Fill** check box is selected and then select the **Interior** and **Reference** check boxes.

4. Choose the **OK** button; the the **Visibility/Graphics Override for Floor Plan1-Mech** dialog box is closed and the added spaces will be displayed with the specified settings, as shown in Figure 4-10.

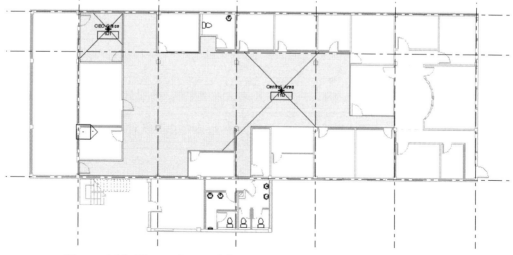

Figure 4-10 *The markers and the interior fills displayed in the added spaces*

Splitting the Space

You need to place a space in the area next to the building entrance because this area will be heated and cooled more often than the rest of the open spaces. The entrance area is considered semi-bounded. To place a space in this area, you need to make it fully-bounded by drawing space separation lines. In this section, you will split the **Central Area** space.

1. Ensure that the **1 - Mech** view is active and enter ZR; the cursor changes into a zoom region icon. Click at the point above the **CEO-Office** space area and drag the mouse downward right below the **Central Area** space, refer to Figure 4-11. and click; the central region of the office area is zoomed.

2. Choose the **Space Separator** tool from the **Spaces & Zones** panel of the **Analyze** tab; the **Modify | Place Space Separation** contextual tab is displayed. In the **Draw** panel of the tab, ensure that the **Line** tool is chosen by default. Also, in the **Options Bar**, ensure that the **Chain** check box is selected and the value specified in the **Offset** edit box is **0'0"** (**0.0**).

3. Now, place the cursor at the endpoint of the space boundary of the **Central Area** near the **Toilet** area, as shown in Figure 4-12. Click when the **Endpoint** snap marker appears; the start point of the separation line is specified.

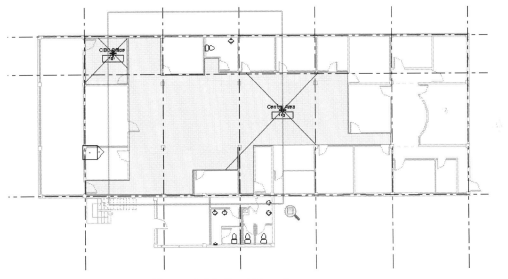

Figure 4-11 *Specifying the zoom area*

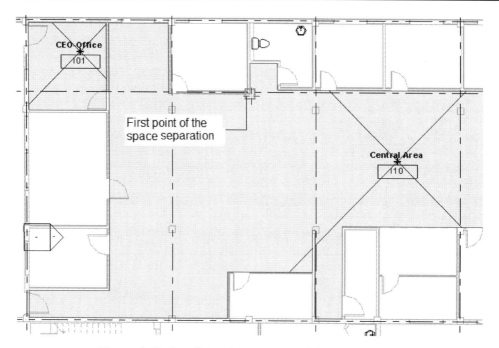

Figure 4-12 Specifying the start point of the separator line

4. Now, move the cursor vertically downward; a dashed line along with temporary dimension appears. Enter **26'5" (8052mm)** and press ENTER; the separation line is created and the **Central Area** is adjusted to the new separation. Now, choose the **Modify** button in the **Select** panel of the **Modify | Place Space Separation** contextual tab to exit the **Space Separator** tool.

On splitting, the central area moves to the proposed lounge area. As such you need to move the splitted space to right toward the actual central area.

5. Select the **Central Area** space by clicking on it. Next, press and drag the left mouse button to move the selected space toward right; the **Autodesk Revit 2019** message box is displayed and the selected space is moved to the actual location.

6. Now, choose the **Move to Space** button in the message box; the message box is closed and the space is placed in the actual location, as shown in Figure 4-13. Choose the **Modify** tool from the **Select** panel of the **Modify|Space** tab to exit the selection.

Note
Space separation lines are MEP-specific room bounding lines that separate areas where a wall is not required or is not possible to create one. After the areas are separated, spaces can be placed in them. Although room separation lines are recognized in Revit, space separation lines are not recognized in Architecture discipline of Revit.

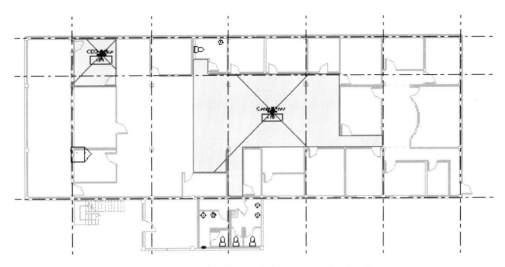

Figure 4-13 *The* **Central Area** *space in the plan*

Placing a Space in the Separated Area

In this section, you will add a space to the area separated from the **Central Area** space.

1. Choose the **Space** tool from the **Spaces & Zones** panel of the **Analyze** tab; the **Modify | Place Space** tab is displayed.

2. In this tab, ensure that the **Tag on Placement** button is chosen. Also, in the **Options Bar**, select the **1-Mech Plenum** from the **Upper Limit** drop-down list and then enter **0"(0.0)** in the **Offset** edit box. In the **Options Bar**, ensure that the **Horizontal** option is selected from the drop-down list displayed next to the **Offset** edit box, the **Leader** check box is cleared, and the **New** option is selected from the **Space** drop-down list.

3. Now, move and place the cursor in the separated area; the room bounding space snap is displayed. Click inside the area, the space is placed in the area.

4. Now, choose the **Modify** button and then select the newly created space; the **Properties** palette displays the instance property of the selected space.

5. In the **Properties** palette, click in the value field corresponding to the **Number** parameter. Next, type **115** and press ENTER.

6. Now, click in the value field of the **Name** parameter. Then, type **Lounge** and press ENTER. Choose the **Modify** button from the **Select** panel of the **Modify| Spaces** tab to exit the modification of the space.

The space number and the name is changed, as shown in Figure 4-14.

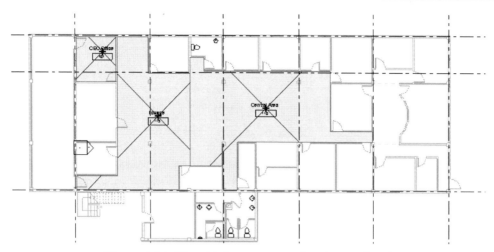

Figure 4-14 *The added space renamed and renumbered*

Placing a Space in the Chases Area

In this section, you will add a space to the chases area. Note that the space components are placed in chases to permit a reliable heating and cooling load analysis.

1.   Zoom in the chases area that is located below the central area, as shown in Figure 4-15.

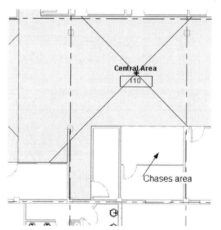

Figure 4-15 *Zooming in the chases area*

2.   Invoke the **Space** tool from the **Spaces & Zones** panel of the **Analyze** tab and then in the **Options Bar**, select **Level 2** from the **Upper Limit** drop-down list.

3.   Click in the **Offset** edit box, enter **1'6" (457mm)**, and press ENTER.

4.   Next, click in the chases area, refer to Figure 4-16, and click when the space snap is highlighted.

5.   Now, choose the **Modify** button from the **Select** panel of the **Modify | Place Space** contextual tab and then select the added space.

6. In the **Properties** palette, enter **Chases** and **121** in the value fields of **Name** and **Number** edit boxes, respectively. Figure 4-16 shows the **Chases** space added to the model.

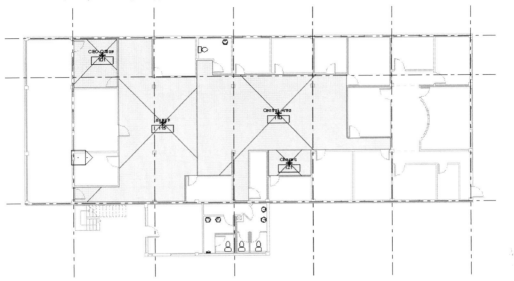

Figure 4-16 Chases space added to the model

7. Choose the **Modify** button from the **Select** panel of the **Modify | Space** contextual tab to exit the selection of the space.

Saving the Project

In this section, you need to save project and settings using the **Save As** tool.

1. To save the project with settings, choose **Save As > Project** from the **File** menu; the **Save As** dialog box is displayed, as you are saving the project for the first time.

2. In this dialog box, browse to the *c:\rmp_2019\c04_rmp_2019_tut* folder and then in the **File name** edit box, enter the text **c04_Office-Space_tut1** (for Metric **M_c04_Office-Space_tut1**) and then choose the **Options** button; the **File Save Options** dialog box is displayed. In this dialog box, ensure that the **Active view/sheet** option is selected from the **Source** drop-down list in the **Thumbnail Preview** area.

3. Now, choose the **OK** button; the **File Save Options** dialog box is closed and the **Save As** dialog box is displayed.

4. In this dialog box, choose the **Save** button to save the current project file with the specified name and close the **Save As** dialog box.

Closing the Project

1. To close the project, choose the **Close** option from **File** menu; the file is closed.

Tutorial 2   Heating and Cooling Load Analysis

In this tutorial, you will perform the Heating and Cooling load analysis of the space model. Also, you will export the model to gbXML file format.   **(Expected time: 45 min)**

File name to be used:
For Imperial: *c04_tut3_analysis_rmp2019*
For Metric: *M_c04_tut3_analysis_rmp2019*

File name to be assigned for export:
For Imperial: *c04_Office-Space_tut3-gb.xml*
For Metric: *M_c04_Office-Space_tut3-gb.xml*

File to be assigned:
For Imperial: *c04_Office-Space_tut3.rvt*
For Metric: *M_c04_Office-Space_tut3.rvt*

The following steps are required to complete this tutorial:

a.   Open the project file.
b.   Specify the project information.
c.   Verify the area and volume settings
d.   Verify the building information.
e.   Verify the space information.
f.   Perform the Heating and Cooling Loads analysis.
g.   Export the model information to *.gbXML* file format.
h.   Save the project using the **Save As** tool.
i.   Close the project by using the **Close** tool.

Opening the Project File

1.   Choose **Open > Project** from the **File** menu; the **Open** dialog box is displayed.

2.   In the dialog box, select the *c04_tut3_analysis_rmp2019.rvt* (for Metric *M_c04_tut3_analysis_ rmp2019.rvt*) file and then choose the **Open** button; the project file is opened.

 Note
*The architectural model named c04_archi_spaces_rmp_2019.rvt linked in this tutorial file is located in the c04_rmp_2019_tut folder. In the **Manage Links** dialog box, it is recommended to assign the **Path Type** of the linked architectural model to **Relative**. However, if the link is lost, you need to reload the file using the **Manage Links** dialog box which has already been discussed in the previous chapters.*

Specifying the Project Information and Location

In this section, you will set the project information and location for the project.

1.   Choose the **Project Information** tool from the **Settings** panel of the **Manage** tab; the **Project Information** dialog box is displayed.

2. In this dialog box, choose the **Edit** button corresponding to the **Energy Settings** parameter; the **Energy Settings** dialog box is displayed. In this dialog box, choose the **Edit** button corresponding to the **Other Options** parameter; the **Advanced Energy Settings** dialog box gets displayed.

3. In this dialog box, ensure that the **Office** option is selected in the **Value** field corresponding to the **Building Type** parameter. Next, retain the default settings for the remaining parameters, refer to Figure 4-17, and then choose the **OK** button; the **Advanced Energy Settings** dialog box gets closed.

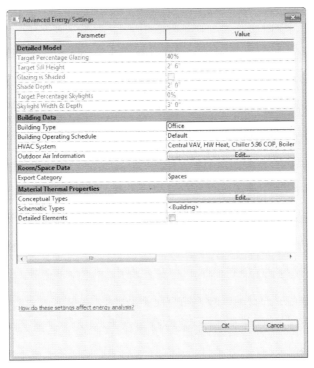

Figure 4-17 *The default values in the* ***Advanced Energy Settings*** *dialog box*

4. Next, in the **Energy Settings** dialog box, retain the default settings for the displayed parameters and then choose the **OK** button; the **Energy Settings** dialog box is closed. Again, choose the **OK** button to close the **Project Information** dialog box.

5. Next, choose the **Location** tool from the **Project Location** panel of the **Manage** tab; the **Location Weather and Site** dialog box is displayed. In this dialog box, ensure that the **Location** tab is chosen by default and then select **Default City List** from the **Define Location by** drop-down list, if it is not selected by default.

6. Now, select the **Indianapolis, IN** option from the **City** drop-down list.

7. In the **Location Weather and Site** dialog box, choose the **Weather** tab and then clear the **Use closest weather station (INDIANAPOLIS)** check box, if it is selected by default.

8. In the **Weather** tab, ensure that **-2 °F (-19 °C)** and **1.0** values are specified in the **Heating Design Temperatures** and **Clearness Number** edit boxes, respectively.

9. Now, choose **OK**; the **Location Weather and Site** dialog box gets closed.

Verifying the Area and Volume Settings

1. Choose the **Area and Volume Computations** tool from the **Spaces & Zones** panel of the **Analyze** tab; the **Area and Volume Computations** dialog box is displayed.

2. In this dialog box, ensure that the **Computations** tab is chosen by default and then in the **Volume Computations** area, select the **Area and Volumes** radio button, if it is not selected by default.

3. In the **Room Area Computation** area, select the **At wall finish** radio button, if it is not selected by default.

4. Now, choose the **OK** button; the **Area and Volume Computations** dialog box gets closed.

 Note
*The **Areas and Volumes** option must be selected for a space to perform an accurate heating and cooling loads analysis.*

Verifying the Building Information

1. Choose the **Heating and Cooling Loads** tool from the **Reports & Schedules** panel of the **Analyze** tab; the **Heating and Cooling Loads** dialog box is displayed. Alternatively, you can type LO to activate the dialog box.

2. In this dialog box, ensure that the **General** tab is chosen by default and then click on the **Value** field corresponding to the **Building Infiltration Class** parameter; a drop-down list is displayed.

3. Select the **Tight** option from the displayed drop-down list.

4. Click on the **Value** field corresponding to the **Report Type** parameter and then select the **Detailed** option from the drop-down list displayed.

5. Select the check box displayed in the **Value** field corresponding to the **Use Load Credits** parameter.

On selecting the **Use Load Credits** check box, the heating or cooling "credit" loads that take the form of negative loads is taken into account for analysis. For example, heat that leaves a zone through a partition into another zone can be a negative load or credit.

After verifying and setting the building information, you will verify and specify the space information of the building.

Verifying the Space Information

1. In the **Heating and Cooling Loads** dialog box, choose the **Details** tab; various options in this tab are displayed.

2. In this tab, ensure that the **Spaces** radio button is selected and then in the list box displayed below the radio button, click on the **Office-Central** node and then expand it. Note that various settings and information for the **Office-Central** zone are displayed below the list box.

3. Now, ensure that the **<Building>** option is selected in the **Service Type** drop-down list, and then choose the browse button next to the **Heating Information** edit box; the **Heating Information** dialog box is displayed.

4. In this dialog box, select the **Humidification Control** check box and then enter **15%** in the **Humidification Set** point edit box.

5. Choose the **OK** button; the **Heating Information** dialog box is closed.

6. Similarly, choose the browse button next to the **Cooling Information** edit box; the **Cooling Information** dialog box is displayed.

7. In the dialog box, select the **Humidification Control** check box and then enter **85%** in the **Dehumidification Set Point** edit box. Choose the **OK** button to close the **Cooling Information** dialog box.

8   Next, click on the **Office-East Zone** node and expand it; various spaces under it are displayed in a hierarchy, as shown in Figure 4-18.

9. To view the spaces in **Office-East Zone**, choose the **Highlight** button displayed on the right of the dialog box, refer to Figure 4-19; various spaces are highlighted in the preview pane displayed in the left pane.

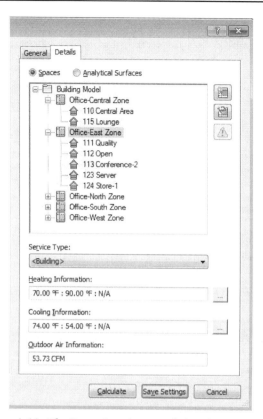

Figure 4-18 *The* **Zone A** *node expanded with various nodes*

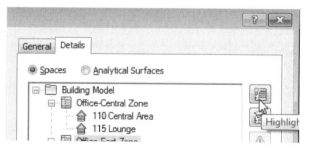

Figure 4-19 *Choosing the* **Highlight** *button*

10. Similarly, select the **Office-North Zone** node; the spaces in the **Office-North Zone** are highlighted in the conceptual model displayed in the preview pane. Now, choose the **Isolate** button displayed below the **Highlight** button in the **Heating and Cooling Loads** dialog box; the spaces in **Office-North Zone** are displayed in isolation from the main conceptual model in the preview pane, as shown in Figure 4-20.

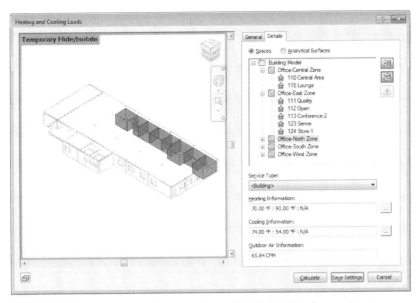

*Figure 4-20 Spaces in the **Zone B** are highlighted in the preview pane*

11. In the **Details** tab, select the **Analytical Surface** radio button and then choose the **Isolate** button again; the analytical model of the project is displayed in the preview pane. Now, choose the **Highlight** button; the analytical conceptual model without the space highlights is displayed in the preview pane, as shown in Figure 4-21. You can use the **ViewCube** tool in the preview pane to rotate the conceptual model and view it from all sides.

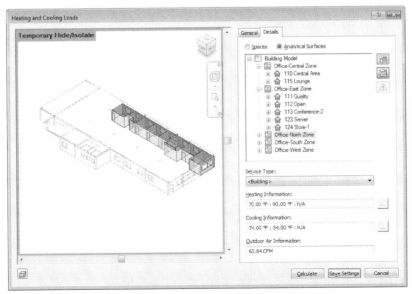

Figure 4-21 The analytical surfaces of the model with space highlights displayed in the preview pane

Tip
*You can use the **View Cube** tool to spin, pan, and zoom the model to have a better view of the space.*

Performing the Heating and Cooling Loads Analysis

1. In the **Heating and Cooling Loads** dialog box, choose the **Calculate** button; the heating and load analysis is performed and the report is displayed in the Load Report(1) tab, as shown in Figure 4-22.

Project Summary

Location and Weather	
Project	Project Name
Address	
Calculation Time	Tuesday, April 17, 2016 12:49 PM
Report Type	Standard
Latitude	42.21°
Longitude	-71.03°
Summer Dry Bulb	92 °F
Summer Wet Bulb	75 °F
Winter Dry Bulb	-2 °F
Mean Daily Range	21 °F

Building Summary

Inputs	
Building Type	Office
Area (SF)	5,447
Volume (CF)	45,636.58
Calculated Results	
Psychrometric Message	One or more zones have psychrometric errors
Peak Cooling Total Load	-
Peak Cooling Month and Hour	-
Peak Cooling Sensible Load	-
Peak Cooling Latent Load	-
Maximum Cooling Capacity	-
Peak Cooling Airflow	-
Peak Heating Load (Btu/h)	109,607.9
Peak Heating Airflow (CFM)	3,965

Figure 4-22 The Heating and Cooling load report

You can scroll down and view the entire report. Also, notice that in the **Project Browser**, the load report is added as the **Loads Report(1)** node under **Reports > Load Reports**, refer to Figure 4-23. You can click on the **Loads Report(1)** node to view the report whenever required.

Revit performs a heating and cooling loads analysis using the integrated heating and cooling loads analysis engine. In this analysis, various factors are analyzed including analytical and inner volumes of the spaces.

2. Review the loads report to analyze the project, weather, space, and zone information of the building model.

Figure 4-23 *The* **Project Browser** *displaying the* **Loads Report(1)** *node*

Note
You must perform a new heating and cooling loads analysis each time you modify building, space, or zone information, or make any changes to the model, otherwise the loads report or schedules will not reflect your changes.

After you have performed the load analysis of the model using the IES engine, you can export the model information to a third party software and compare the results. To export the model information to a third party software, you need to create a gbXML file.

Exporting the Model Information to gbXML File
In this section, you will export the model information into gbXML file format.

1. Choose **Default 3D View** tool from **View > Create > 3DView** drop-down; the 3d view of the project is displayed in the {**3D**} tab. Choose **Export > gbXML** from the **File** menu; the **Export gbXML** dialog box is displayed.

2. In the dialog box, select the **Use Room/Space Volumes** radio button and then choose **OK**; the **Export gbXML Settings** dialog box is displayed.

3. Retain all the default settings in the dialog box and then choose the **Next** button; the **Export gbXML -Save to Target Folder** dialog box is displayed.

4. Browse to the *C:\rmp_2019\c04_rmp_2019_tut* folder and type **c04_office-space-tut3-gb** (for Metric, **M_c04_office-space-tut3-gb**)in the **File name** edit box. Choose **Save**; the file is saved in the *.xml* file format.

Saving the Project
In this section, you need to save the project and settings using the **Save As** tool.

1. To save the project with the settings, choose **Save As > Project** from the **File** menu; the **Save As** dialog box is displayed as you are saving the project for the first time,.

2. In this dialog box, browse to the *C:\rmp_2019\c04_rmp_2019_tut* folder and then in the **File name** edit box, enter **c04_Office-Space_tut3** (for Metric, **M_c04_Office-Space_tut3**)and then choose the **Options** button; the **File Save Options** dialog box is displayed.

3. Now, choose the **OK** button; the **File Save Options** dialog box is closed and the **Save As** dialog box is displayed.

4. In the displayed dialog box, choose the **Save** button to save the current project file with the specified name.

Closing the Project

1. To close the project, choose the **Close** option from the **File** menu; the file is closed.

EXERCISE

Exercise 1   Creating Spaces

Download the *c04_Conference-Center_exer1.rvt* (for Metric *M_c04_Conference-Center_exer1.rvt*)file from *http://www.cadsofttech.com*. The path of the file is as follows: *Textbooks > Civil/GIS > Revit > Exploring Autodesk Revit 2019 for MEP.*

In this exercise, you will open an architectural model and then add spaces to it. Name and number the spaces, as shown in Figure 4-24.

Note
You can add properties to the spaces as per your design requirement.

1. Project view to be used :
             Views > Floor Plans > Mechanical > 1ST FLOOR- HVAC Space

2. File name to be assigned: *c04_Conference-Center_exer1a.rvt* (For Metric *M_c04_Conference-Center_exer1a.rvt*).

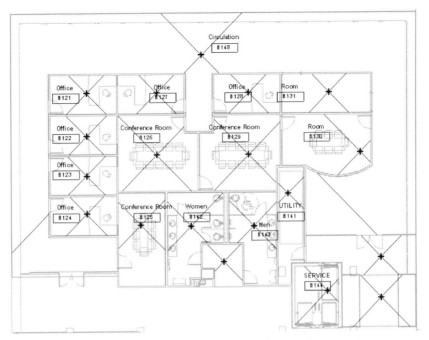

Figure 4-24 Spaces created for the Conference-Center project

This page is intenionally left blank

Chapter 5

Creating an HVAC System

Learning Objectives

After completing this chapter, you will be able to:

- *Create an HVAC system*
- *Generate an HVAC system layout*
- *Create ducts and duct fittings*

INTRODUCTION

Heating, Ventilation, and Air Conditioning (HVAC) is the technology of indoor and vehicular environmental comfort. The goal of HVAC is to provide thermal comfort and acceptable indoor air quality. It is one of the most important factors for maintaining acceptable indoor air quality in buildings.

In this chapter, you will learn about various tools and options to create HVAC systems for a project. In Revit, you can use different tools to create, modify, and inspect HVAC systems in a project. These tools allow you to model and analyze systems and check whether your project design values meet the engineering standards fixed by the organization you are working with.

CREATING AN HVAC SYSTEM

In an MEP project, the HVAC system is designed for three important functions, namely heating, ventilating, and air conditioning of a building. These three functions are closely interrelated and the design, installation, and control systems of these functions are integrated into one or more HVAC systems in a project.

While working in an HVAC system for an MEP project, you will place air terminals and mechanical equipment. Next, you will create supply, return, and exhaust systems to connect the components of the HVAC system and create system groups.

In Revit, you create the HVAC systems using different tools available in the **HVAC**, **Fabrication**, and **Mechanical** panels of the **Systems** tab, as shown in Figure 5-1. Apart from these tools, you can use automatic system creation tools to create duct routing layouts to connect the supply and return system components to the HVAC system.

Figure 5-1 *Various tools in the* *Systems* *panel*

Recommended Practices for Creating HVAC Systems

While working in an HVAC system, there are certain recommended practices that help you to create HVAC systems effectively. These practices are as follows:

1. While placing air terminals and equipment, it is recommended to copy the existing air terminals and equipment to the desired locations. This will help the copied elements in inheriting the properties such as elevation and type from the parent element. This practice will save time because you do not have to specify similar information for multiple components.

2. It is always recommended to schedule information related to spaces in the project, which will be useful during the design process of the HVAC system, irrespective of whether the information will become part of the design documentation or not.

3. While scheduling information for the spaces in the project, it is always recommended to use conditional formatting in the schedules that you create to identify design problems.

4. It is recommended to use the schedule views to update the properties of different equipment. This practice will quickly update multiple components without selecting and editing the components in the drawing.

GENERATING HVAC SYSTEM LAYOUTS

After you create an HVAC system, you will add different components to it and use automatic layout tools to review possible routing solutions. The automatic layout tools will provide you with multiple layout solutions that you can explore to suit your design requirement. If you do not find the required set of connections, you can manually modify the layout path solutions.

An HVAC system layout is a representation of the physical connection between different components in an HVAC system. For example, you can create duct layouts to connect air system components. Revit will provide you with tools to generate the layout of the ductwork automatically when components are added to the HVAC systems.

While creating a system layout, only those components will be considered that are connected to the same system and are displayed in the plan view. If you select a component in 3D, section, or elevation view, all components that are connected to the same system, even if they reside on the multiple levels, will be considered for the layout. This is important when you create a layout for components that are connected to the same system but are located on different levels.

While generating layouts using the automatic layout tool, you will notice that each layout solution consists of blue and green layout lines. Blue lines represent the main duct layout, and green lines represent the branches duct layout. You can generate three types of routing solutions for a layout: Network, Perimeter, and Intersection.

CREATING DUCTS AND DUCT FITTINGS

In an HVAC system, the ducts are used to supply and remove air from a space. The airflow inside the ducts includes supply air, return air, and exhaust air.

In Revit, the ducts are created using the automatic connection snaps. When you place the duct segments in a project, Revit automatically connects two segments of the ducts with appropriate duct fittings. This method saves your time as there will be no need to join or trim elements.

Creating Ducts

To create a duct segment in a drawing, open the desired view from the **Project Browser** and then choose the **Duct** tool from the **HVAC** panel in the **Systems** tab; the **Modify | Place Duct** contextual tab will be displayed, as shown in Figure 5-2.

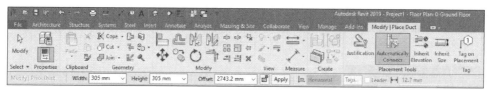

*Figure 5-2 Different options in the **Modify / Place Duct** contextual tab*

TUTORIALS
General instructions for downloading tutorial files:

1. Download the *c05_rmp_2019_tut.zip* file for this tutorial from *http://www.cadsofttech.com*. The path of the file is as follows: *Textbooks > Civil/GIS > Revit MEP > Revit MEP 2019 for Novices*.

2. Now, save and extract the downloaded zip file at the following location: *C:\rmp_2019\ c05_rmp_2019_tut*

Note
The default unit system used in the tutorials is Imperial.

Tutorial 1   Placing Air Terminals

In this tutorial, you will place air terminals in the ceiling of the rooms. Also, you will create new views, modify air terminal parameters, and place air terminals in the ceiling plan.

(Expected time: 45 min)

1. File to be used: *c05_Office-Space_tut1.rvt (M_c05_Office-Space_tut1.rvt)*
2. File name to be assigned: *c05_Office-Space_tut1a.rvt (M_c05_Office-Space_tut1a.rvt)*

The following steps are required to complete this tutorial:

a. Open the *05_Office-Space_tut1.rvt (M_05_Office-Space_tut1.rvt)* file.
b. Modify the ceiling plan.
c. Add the supply air terminal.
d. Add the return and exhaust air terminal.
e. Save the project by using the **Save As** tool.
f. Close the project using the **Close** tool.

Opening the Project
In this section, you will open the *c05_Office-Space_tut1.rvt (M_ c05_Office-Space_tut1.rvt)* file
.

1. Choose **Open > Project** from the **File** menu; the **Open** dialog box is displayed.

2. In the **Open** dialog box, browse to *C:\rmp_2019\c05_rmp_2019_tut* and select the *c05_Office-Space_tut1.rvt. (M_c05_Office-Space_tut1.rvt)* file. Now, choose the **Open** button; the selected file opens in the Revit.

Note
The architectural model named c04_archi_spaces_rmp_2019.rvt (for Metric M_c04_archi_spaces_rmp_2019.rvt) linked in this tutorial file is located in the c04_rmp_2019_tut folder.

*While linking a model to the project in Revit, it is recommended to maintain the relative path as the path type for the link. However, if the link is lost, you need to reload the file using the **Manage Links** dialog box which has already been discussed in the previous chapters.*

Modifying the Ceiling Plan View

In this section, you will modify the ceiling plan view using the **View Range** dialog box.

1   In the **Project Browser**, expand **Views (Discipline) > Mechanical > HVAC > Ceiling Plans**, and double-click on **1 - Ceiling Mech** to make it an active view.

2.   In the **Properties** palette, choose the **Edit** button corresponding to the **View Range** parameter under the **Extents** head; the **View Range** dialog box is displayed.

3.   In the **Primary Range** area of this dialog box, select the **Associated Level (Level1)** option from the **Top** drop-down list and then enter **8' 4" (2540mm)** in the **Offset** edit box.

4.   Enter **0** in the **Offset** edit box corresponding to the **Cut plane** drop-down list.

5.   In the **View Depth** area of the **View Range** dialog box, select the **Associated Level (Level 1)** option from the **Level** drop-down list and enter **8' 4" (2540mm)** in the **Offset** edit box corresponding to the **Level** drop-down list.

6.   Choose **Apply** and then **OK**; the specified settings are applied to the current view and the **View Range** dialog box is closed.

Note
On modifying the ranges of the ceiling plan view, the fixtures and fittings that will be placed in the model will be visible.

Adding the Supply Air Terminal

In this section, you will place the supply air terminals in the ceiling of the rooms.

1.   Choose the **Air Terminal** tool from the **HVAC** panel of the **Systems** tab; the **Modify | Place Air Terminal** contextual tab is displayed.

2.   Choose the **Load Family** tool from the **Mode** panel of the contextual tab; the **Load Family** dialog box is displayed.

3.   In the dialog box, browse to **US Imperial > Mechanical > MEP > Air Side Components > Air Terminals** folder (for Metric, browse to **US Metric > Mechanical > MEP > Air Side Components > Air Terminals** folder) and then select the **Supply Diffuser - Hosted (M_Supply Diffuser-Hosted)** family from the list displayed.

4.   Next, choose **Open**; the **Load Family** dialog box is closed and the selected family is loaded in the project file.

5. In the **Properties** palette, select the **Supply Diffuser - Hosted: Workplane-based Supply Diffuser** option (for Metric **M_SupplyDiffuser - Hosted: Workplane-based Supply Diffuser**) from the **Type Selector** drop-down list.

6. In the **Placement** panel of the **Modify | Place Air Terminal** contextual tab, choose the **Place on Face** button.

7. In the drawing area, move the cursor toward the upper left corner of the plan into the **CEO-Office** area and click to place at the location shown in Figure 5-3.

Figure 5-3 The supply air terminal placed in the CEO-Office area

Note
The air terminal will be placed on the ceiling.

8. In the **Properties** palette, enter **300 CFM** (**150 L/S**) in the edit box corresponding to the **Flow** parameter under the **Mechanical - Flow** head.

9. Now, choose the **Modify** button from the **Select** panel to exit the **Air Terminal** tool.

10. Select the added air terminal and place the cursor at the center grip of the air terminal; the center grip turns red and the **Drag** tooltip appears. Press the left mouse button and drag the air terminal to fit it inside the ceiling tile, as shown in Figure 5-4.

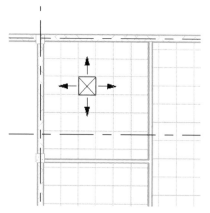

Figure 5-4 Placing the supply air terminal inside the ceiling tile

11. After placing the air terminal, release the left mouse button.

12. Next, ensure that the air terminal is selected and then choose the **Copy** tool from the **Modify** panel; a dashed box is displayed around the selected air terminal.

13. In the **Options Bar**, select the **Multiple** check box.

14. In the drawing area, place the cursor at the center of the air terminal and click when the **Midpoint** snap is displayed, as shown in Figure 5-5.

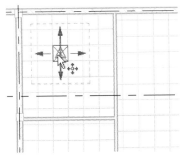

Figure 5-5 Placing the cursor at the center of the air terminal

15. Move the cursor vertically down and click when the vertical dimension appears as **12'** **(3658mm)** and the angle shows **90.000°**, as shown in Figure 5-6. Similarly, copy and place the other air terminals at required locations, as shown in Figure 5-7.

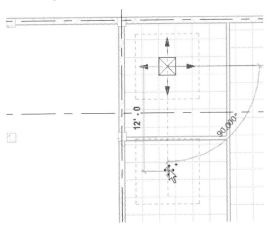

Figure 5-6 Copying the air terminal to the other area

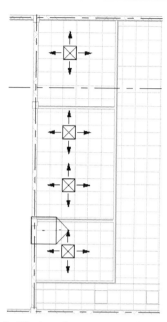

Figure 5-7 *Placing the air terminals in other areas*

Note
The placement of the air terminals may not be exact.

16. Choose the **Modify** tool from the **Select** panel to exit the tool.

Adding the Return and Exhaust Air Terminal
In this section, you will add the return and exhaust air terminal to the architectural layout.

1. Choose the **Air Terminal** tool from the **HVAC** panel of the **Systems** tab; the **Modify | Place Air Terminal** contextual tab is displayed.

2. Choose the **Load Family** tool from the **Mode** panel of the contextual tab; the **Load Family** dialog box is displayed.

3. In the dialog box, browse to **US Imperial > Mechanical > MEP > Air Side Components > Air Terminals** folder (for Metric, browse to **US Metric > Mechanical > MEP > Air Side Components > Air Terminals** folder) and then using the CTRL key, select the **Exhaust Diffuser - Hosted (M_Exhaust Diffuser-Hosted)** and **Return Diffuser - Hosted** families **(M_Return Diffuser-Hosted)** from the list displayed.

4. Choose **Open**; the selected families are loaded in the file and the **Load Family** dialog box is closed.

5. In the **Properties** palette, select the **Return Diffuser - Hosted: Workplane-based Return Diffuser** option (for Metric, select the **M_ Return Diffuser - Hosted: Workplane-based Return Diffuser** option) from the **Type Selector** drop-down list.

6. In the **Properties** palette, click in the value field corresponding to the **Flow** parameter and enter **300 CFM** (for Metric, **150 L/S**).

7. Choose the **Place on Face** button from the **Placement** panel in the **Modify|Place Air Terminal** contextual tab.

8. Next, in the drawing area, move the cursor in the Lounge area next to the CEO-Office room and then click inside the ceiling tile, as shown in Figure 5-8.

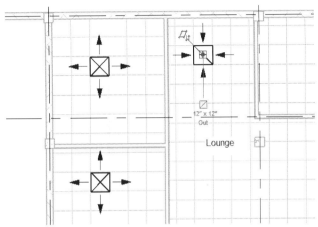

Figure 5-8 Placing the return air terminal in the Lounge area

9. Now, click inside the ceiling tile in the Lounge area to place the other return air terminals, as shown in Figure 5-9.

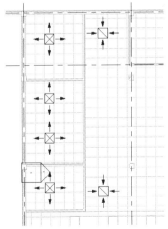

Figure 5-9 Placing the other return air terminal in the Lounge area

10. Next, in the **Properties** palette, select the **Exhaust Diffuser - Hosted: Workplane-based Exhaust Diffuser** type (for Metric, select the **M_Exhaust Diffuser - Hosted: Workplane-based Exhaust Diffuser**) from the **Type Selector** drop-down list.

11. In the **Properties** palette, click in the value field corresponding to the **Flow** parameter and enter **250 CFM** (for Metric, **120 L/S**).

12. In the drawing area, move the cursor to the Toilet 1 area, and click inside the ceiling tile at the location, as shown in Figure 5-10, to place the exhaust air terminal.

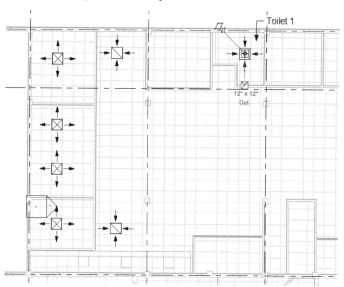

Figure 5-10 Placing the exhaust air terminal in the Toilet 1 area

13. Choose the **Modify** button from the **Select** panel to exit the tool.

 Note
You can add more air terminals to complete the requirement of the HVAC system in the Office-Space area.

After you place the return and exhaust air terminals, remember to modify the airflow display arrows for air terminals that requires 2-way and 3-way blow patterns by setting the **UpArrow**, **RightArrow**, **LeftArrow**, and **DownArrow** parameters from the **Properties** palette

Saving and Closing the Project

In this section, you need to save the project and the settings using the **Save As** tool.

1. Choose **Save As > Project** from **File** menu. As you are saving the project for the first time, the **Save As** dialog box is displayed.

2. In this dialog box, browse to *C:\rmp_2019\c05_rmp_2019_tut* and in the **File name** edit box, enter **c05_Office-Space_tut1a** (**M_c05_Office-Space_tut1a**) and then choose the **Save** button to save the current project file with the specified name and to close the **Save As** dialog box.

3. Choose the **Close** option from the **File** menu.

EXERCISE

Exercise 1   HVAC System

Download the *c05_Conference-Center_exer1.rvt* (for Metric *M_c05_Conference-Center_exer1.rvt*) file from *http://www.cadsofttech.com*. The path of the file is as follows: *Textbooks > Civil/GIS > Revit MEP > Revit MEP 2019 For Novices*.

Open the *c05_Conference-Center_exer1.rvt* file and create an HVAC system in the conference room for the *Conference-Center* project. While creating the HVAC system, you will add air terminals to the spaces, as shown in Figure 5-11. You will also create the duct system for the air terminals, as shown in Figure 5-12.

(Note : 1 CFM = 0.47 L/s)

1. Project view to be used :
                Floor Plans > Mechanical > 1ST FLOOR- HVAC DUCT

2. Family type to be used:
    Air Terminals
                For Imperial   Rectangular Diffuser- Round Connection : 24*24 -10 Neck
                For Metric   M_Supply Diffuser - Rectangular Face Round Neck :
                                    600*600 - 250 Neck

    Duct System
                For Imperial   Rectangular Duct : Galvanized
                For Metric   Rectangular Duct : Galvanized
3. File name to be assigned: *c05_Conference-Center_exer1a.rvt*

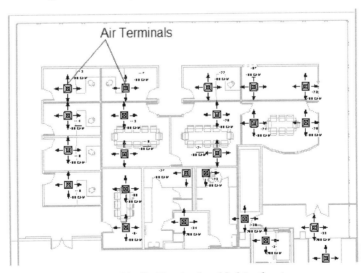

Figure 5-11 Air Terminals added in the space

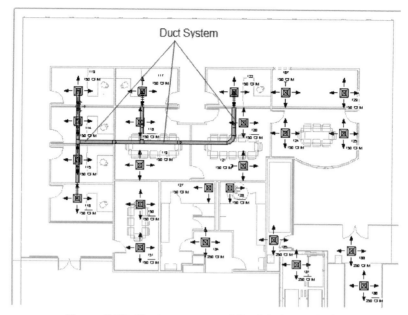

Figure 5-12 Duct system created for the air terminals

Chapter 6

Creating an Electrical System

Learning Objectives

After completing this chapter, you will be able to:

- *Add electrical equipments*
- *Add power and system devices*
- *Add lighting fixtures*
- *Specify electrical settings*
- *Create power distribution systems*
- *Perform lighting analysis*
- *Add electrical circuits and wires*

INTRODUCTION

In this chapter, you will learn about various procedures and tools available in Revit (MEP) to create an electrical system in a project. You will learn to add various power and system devices and lighting fixtures. You will also learn to modify various electrical settings, add conduits, cable trays, and specify the Power Distribution System for a project.

ADDING ELECTRICAL EQUIPMENT

In an MEP project, the electrical equipment consists of panels and transformers. This equipment plays an important role in the functioning of the building. The process of adding electrical equipment in a building is discussed next.

Adding Transformers

A transformer is an electrical equipment that is used to transform power from one circuit to another without changing the frequency of the input current. The primary use of transformer in a building is to transform the electricity from one voltage to another (generally from higher to lower) and distribute the electricity in the circuits of the building. In general, transformers are essential for the transmission, distribution, and utilization of electrical energy in a building project.

In Revit (MEP), you can model and add transformers of various sizes with different ratings and voltage requirement. In a project, you can represent a transformer as a symbol or as a physical model. The transformer that you will add can be added in a floor or can be mounted in the wall. In Revit, you can add both wet and dry transformers. Figure 6-1 shows a general purpose dry type transformer of the following specification: construction encapsulated, primary voltage 240 x 480 V, and NEMA 3R.

Figure 6-1 *A dry type transformer of 240 x 480 V, NEMA 3R*

ADDING POWER AND SYSTEM DEVICES

Devices consist of receptacles, switches, junction boxes, telephones, communications, and data terminal devices, nurse call devices, wall speakers, starters, smoke detectors, and fire alarm manual pull stations. Electrical devices are often hosted components (receptacles that must be placed on a wall or work plane). Figure 6-2 shows various electrical devices that can be used in an electrical system of a project.

Figure 6-2 *Various electrical devices*

ADDING LIGHTING FIXTURES

In a project, a light fixture (US English), or light fitting (UK English), or luminaire (IEC, International Electrotechnical Commission) is an electrical device which will be used to create artificial light by using various types of electric lamps. A light fixture comprises of a fixture body and a light socket that will hold the lamp and allow its replacement on requirement.

A light fixture will also require a switch to control the light and an electrical connection to a power source. In a project, light fixture can be moveable or fixed at a point. A light fixture can also have other features, such as reflectors for directing the light, an aperture (with or without a lens), an outer shell or housing for lamp alignment and protection, and an electrical ballast or power supply. The classification of light fixture is based on the fixture installation, the function of the light, and the type of lamp.

CREATING POWER DISTRIBUTION SYSTEM

After you place all the electrical components and equipment in a project, the next step will be to create a system to set a path for the flow of electricity through them. The system that you will create between various electrical panels and the transformer will be called as Power Distribution System.

To create a power distribution system, you need to create a distributive relationship between the transformer and the panels. This relationship will enable you to track loads from the branch circuit panels to the main electrical equipment. You will learn the creation of distribution system from the example given next.

In this example, you will create a power distribution system between a transformer and two panels. To do so, you need to first place the transformer and the panels in the project view.

PERFORMING LIGHTING ANALYSIS

Lighting analysis is used to help you plan the type of light fixtures that will be added to the project. You can create a schedule of the spaces in the project that will display the light fixtures and the lighting criteria for the project. Further, you can review this schedule while placing light fixtures. This will enable you to analyze the difference between the planned and actual requirement of illumination of the spaces due to the light fixtures. Figure 6-3 shows a simple version of this type of schedule. The last column is a calculated value that shows the difference between the required lighting level and the actual level. A difference greater than 6 footcandles causes the cell to turn brown. Since there are no lights in the model yet, none of the spaces have the required lighting level. Hence every cell in the column appears brown. The objective of a lighting designer will be to achieve a schedule with no brown cells in the final stage. The procedure of performing the lighting analysis has been discussed in the Tutorial 1 of this Chapter.

				<Lighting Analysis>				
A	B	C	D	E	F	G	H	I
Required Illuminati	Average Estimated Illumination	Ceiling Reflectanc	Floor Reflectance	Lighting Calculatio	Name	Number	Wall Reflectance	Delta
30 fc	15 fc	0.75	20.00%	2' - 6"	CEO-Office	101	0.50	15.67 fc
30 fc	0 fc	0.75	20.00%	2' - 6"	V.P. Marketing	102	0.50	30.00 fc
30 fc	0 fc	0.75	20.00%	2' - 6"	Toilet-1	103	0.50	30.00 fc
30 fc	0 fc	0.75	20.00%	2' - 6"	Rest Room	104	0.50	30.00 fc
30 fc	0 fc	0.75	20.00%	2' - 6"	Cafeteria	105	0.50	30.00 fc
20 fc	0 fc	0.75	20.00%	2' - 6"	Store	106	0.50	20.00 fc
30 fc	0 fc	0.75	20.00%	2' - 6"	Purchase	107	0.50	30.00 fc
30 fc	0 fc	0.75	20.00%	2' - 6"	International	108	0.50	30.00 fc
30 fc	0 fc	0.75	20.00%	2' - 6"	H.R.	109	0.50	30.00 fc
45 fc	0 fc	0.75	20.00%	2' - 6"	Central Area	110	0.50	45.00 fc
30 fc	0 fc	0.75	20.00%	2' - 6"	Quality	111	0.50	30.00 fc
20 fc	0 fc	0.75	20.00%	2' - 6"	Open	112	0.50	20.00 fc
35 fc	0 fc	0.75	20.00%	2' - 6"	Conference-2	113	0.50	35.00 fc
35 fc	0 fc	0.75	20.00%	2' - 6"	Conference	114	0.50	35.00 fc
25 fc	0 fc	0.75	20.00%	2' - 6"	Lounge	115	0.50	25.00 fc
35 fc	0 fc	0.75	20.00%	2' - 6"	Meeting Room	116	0.50	35.00 fc
30 fc	0 fc	0.75	20.00%	2' - 6"	Service-1	117	0.50	30.00 fc
20 fc	0 fc	0.75	20.00%	2' - 6"	Shaft	118	0.50	20.00 fc
20 fc	0 fc	0.75	20.00%	2' - 6"	Service-2	119	0.50	20.00 fc
30 fc	0 fc	0.75	20.00%	2' - 6"	Accounts	120	0.50	30.00 fc

Figure 6-3 *A typical lighting schedule*

CREATING CIRCUITS

In the electrical system for a project, circuits are the sub-systems that Revit will use for electrical design. In a project, the circuit can be created for devices or fixtures without selecting a panel. While working in a project, it is important to demarcate the difference between wires and circuits. Circuits are the actual connection between devices or fixtures whereas the wires are representation of these connections, symbolically.

ADDING WIRES TO THE CIRCUIT

In a project, you can draw the wires for the circuit manually. To add the wires in the project, you can choose any of the following tools: Arc Wire, Spline Wire, and Chamfered Wire. You can choose any of these tools from **Systems > Electrical > Wire** drop-down. To draw an arc shaped wire, choose the **Arc Wire** tool; the **Modify | Place Wire** tool will be displayed. In the **Tag** panel of this tab, choose the **Tag on Placement** button to display the tag with the wires. In the **Properties** palette, you can select the type of the wire from the **Type Selector** drop-down list. Next, in the drawing view, click at a desired point to specify the start point of the wire. Now, click at a point to define the second point of the arc. To complete the sketch of the arc wire, click at a desired point in the drawing area to specify the end point of the wire; the wire will be created. You can modify the instance properties of the wire by using the various parameters displayed in the **Properties** palette. After modifying the instance properties of the wire, choose **Modify** from the **Select** panel to exit the tool. Similarly, you can create a spline or chamfered wire by using the **Spline Wire** and **Chamfered Wire** tools from **Systems > Electrical > Wire** drop-down, respectively.

TUTORIALS
General instructions for downloading tutorial files:

1. Download the *c06_rmp_2019_tut.zip* file for this tutorial from *http://www.cadsofttech.com*. The path of the file is as follows: *Textbooks > Civil/GIS > Revit MEP > Revit MEP 2019 For Novices*.

2. Now, save and extract the downloaded folder at the following location:
   C:\rmp_2019\c06_rmp_2019_tut

Tutorial 1   Planning the Electrical Systems

In this tutorial, you will specify the settings for the electrical system and also load the family components required for the project.   **(Expected time: 45 min)**

1. File to be used:
   - For Imperial: *c06_archi_elec_tut1.rvt*
   - For Metric: *M_c06_archi-elec_tut1.rvt*

2. File name to be assigned:
   - For Imperial   *c06_Office-Space_tut1a.rvt*
   - For Metric   *M_c06_Office-Space_tut1a.rvt*

The following steps are required to complete this tutorial:

a. Open the *c06_archi_elec_tut1.rvt* (For Metric *M_c06_archi_elec_tut1.rvt*) project file.
b. Specify the electrical settings.
c. Load family components.
d. Save the project.
e. Close the project.

Opening the Project File
1. Choose **Open > Project** from the **File** menu; the **Open** dialog box is displayed.

2. In the dialog box, browse to *c:\rmp_2019\c06_rmp_2019_tut* folder and then select the *c06_archi_elec_tut1.rvt* (*M_ c06_archi_elec_tut1.rvt*) file. Next, choose the **Open** button; the project file is opened.

 Note
*The architectural model named c04_archi_spaces_rmp_2019.rvt (for Metric M_c04_archi_ spaces_rmp_2019.rvt) linked in this tutorial file is located in the c04_rmp_2019_tut folder. It is recommended to maintain the relative path to the architectural model. However, if the link is lost, you need to reload the file using the **Manage Links** dialog box which has already been discussed in the previous chapters.*

Specifying Electrical Settings
1. Choose the **Electrical Settings** button from the **Electrical** panel of the **Systems** tab; the **Electrical Settings** dialog box is displayed.

2. In the left pane of this dialog box, click on **Wiring > Wiring Types** node; a table is displayed.

3. Choose the **Add** button in the dialog box; a new row is displayed in the table.

4. In this row, specify the settings as follows:

    Name: **AL-THHN**   Material: **Aluminium**   Temperature Rating: **75**
    Insulation: **THHN**   Max Size: **500**   Neutral Multiplier: **1.00**
    Neutral Required: Select the check box   Conduit Type: **Steel**
    Neutral Size: **Hot Conductor Size**

5. Next, in the left pane of the dialog box, select the **Voltage Definitions** node; a table is displayed.

6. In the table, retain the default settings for all the parameters, refer to Figure 6-4.

	Name	Value	Minimum	Maximum
1	120	120.00 V	110.00 V	130.00 V
2	208	208.00 V	200.00 V	220.00 V
3	240	240.00 V	220.00 V	250.00 V
4	277	277.00 V	260.00 V	280.00 V
5	480	480.00 V	460.00 V	490.00 V

*Figure 6-4 The table displaying the specified parameter for the **Voltage Definitions** node*

7. In the left pane of the dialog box, select the **Distribution Systems** node; a table is displayed in the right pane.

8. Retain the default settings in this table, as shown in Figure 6-5.

	Name	Phase	Configuration	Wires	L-L Voltage	L-G Voltage
1	120/208 Wye	Three	Wye	4	208	120
2	120/240 Single	Single	None	3	240	120
3	480/277 Wye	Three	Wye	4	480	277

*Figure 6-5 The table displaying the specified parameter for the **Distribution Systems** node*

9. In the left pane of the dialog box, click on the **Load Calculations** node; various options related to the calculations of the electrical load are displayed in the right pane.

10. In the right pane, choose the **Load Classifications** button; the **Load Classifications** dialog box is displayed, as shown in Figure 6-6.

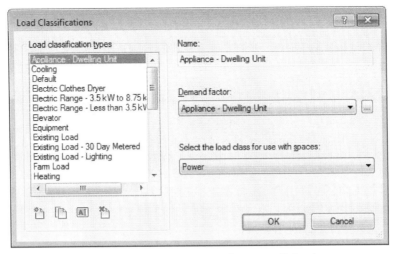

*Figure 6-6 The **Load Classifications** dialog box*

11. In the **Load classification types** area of this dialog box, select the **Other** option and then in the right side of the dialog box, ensure that the **Other** option is selected in the **Demand Factor** drop-down list.

12. Choose the browse button displayed next to the **Demand factor** drop-down list; the **Demand Factors** dialog box is displayed, as shown in Figure 6-7.

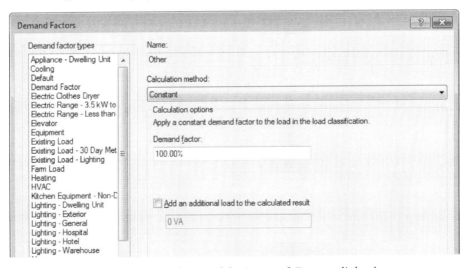

*Figure 6-7 Partial view of the **Demand Factors** dialog box*

13. In this dialog box, ensure that the **Other** option is selected in the **Demand factor types** area and then select the **By load** option from the **Calculation method** drop-down list; a table is displayed below it.

14. In the **Calculation options** area, select the **Incrementally for each range** radio button and then choose the **Split the selected row** button (icon displayed in '**+**' symbol) twice. On doing so, two rows are added to the table, refer to Figure 6-8.

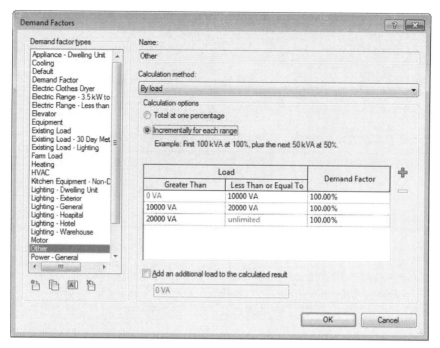

Figure 6-8 The rows added in the table

15. Now, assign the settings in this table, as given in Figure 6-9.

Load		Demand Factor
Greater Than	Less Than or Equal To	
0 VA	2000 VA	100.00%
2000 VA	70000 VA	50.00%
70000 VA	unlimited	30.00%

Figure 6-9 The settings specified in the rows added

16. Choose **OK**; the **Demand Factors** dialog box is closed. Next, choose **OK** twice in the **Load Classifications** and **Electrical Settings** dialog boxes to close them.

Loading the Electrical Components

1. Choose the **Load Family** tool from the **Load from Library** panel of the **Insert** tab; the **Load Family** dialog box is displayed.

2. In the dialog box, browse to **US Imperial > Electrical > MEP > Electric Power > Distribution** folder (for Metric, browse to **US Metric > Electrical > MEP > Electric Power > Distribution**) and then select the *Lighting and Appliance Panelboard - 208V MLO - Surface.rfa* (for Metric, *M_ Lighting and Appliance Panelboard - 208V MLO - Surface.rfa*) file from it.

3. Press and hold the CTRL key, and then select the *Lighting and Appliance Panelboard - 480V MCB - Surface.rfa* (for Metric, *M_Lighting and Appliance Panelboard - 480V MCB - Surface.rfa*) file.

4. Choose the **Open** button; the **Load Family** dialog box is closed and the selected families are loaded in the project.

5. Repeat Steps 1 and 2 and select the other family files required for this tutorial from their respective folders. Refer to the table given next for the name of the file and their folder locations.

Name of the Family(ies)	Folder Location
Duplex Receptacle, Lighting Switches (for Metric M_Duplex Receptacle, M_Lighting Switches)	US Imperial > Electrical > MEP > Electric Power > Terminals (for Metric US Metric > Electrical > MEP > Electric Power > Terminals)
Dry Type Transformer - 480-208Y120 - NEMA Type 2 (for Metric M_Dry Type Transformer - 480-208Y120 - NEMA Type 2)	US Imperial > Electrical > MEP > Electric Power > Generation and Transformation (US Metric > Electrical > MEP > Electric Power > Generation and Transformation)
Troffer Corner Insert (for Metric M_ Troffer Corner Insert)	US Imperial > Lighting > MEP > Internal (US Metric > Lighting > MEP > Internal)

Saving and Closing the Project
In this section, you need to save the project and the settings.

1. Choose **Save As > Project** from **File Menu**; the **Save As** dialog box is displayed.

2. In this dialog box, browse to the *C:\rmp_2019\c06_rmp_2019_tut* folder and then in the **File name** edit box, enter the text **c06_Office-Space_tut1a** (for Metric, **M_c06_Office-Space_ tut1a**) and then choose the **Save** button to save the current project file with the specified name and to close the **Save As** dialog box.

3. Choose the **Close** option from **File** menu; the file is closed.

Tutorial 2   Analyzing the Illumination Requirement

In this tutorial, you will analyze the illumination level required for the different spaces in the office-space building. This analysis will then be used for designing the electrical system for the office-space building.   **(Expected time: 1hr 15 min)**

1. File to be used:
    - For Imperial: *c06_Office-Space_tut1a.rvt*
    - For Metric: *M_06_Office-Space_tut1a .rvt*

2. File name to be assigned:
    - For Imperial: *c06_Office-Space_tut2.rvt*
    - For Metric: *M_c06_Office-Space_tut2.rvt*

The following steps are required to complete this tutorial:

a. Open the *c06_Office-Space_tut1a .rvt* (*M_c06_Office-Space_tut1a.rvt*) project file.
b. Define the required illumination parameter.
c. Create a key schedule for the required illumination level.
d. Enter the required illumination level.
e. Assign the space keys to the spaces.
f. Assign space color fills.
g. Compare the illumination level.
h. Save and Close the project.

Opening the Project File
1. Choose **Open > Project** from the **File** menu; the **Open** dialog box is displayed.

2. In the dialog box, browse to th*e c:\rmp_2019\c06_rmp_2019_tut* folder and then select the *c06_Office-Space_tut1a.rvt* (*M_06_Office-Space_tut1a.rvt*) file and then choose the **Open** button; the project file is opened.

Defining the Required Illumination Level Parameter
1. Choose the **Project Parameters** tool from the **Settings** panel of the **Manage** tab; the **Project Parameters** dialog box is displayed.

2. In the **Project Parameters** dialog box, choose the **Add** button; the **Parameter Properties** dialog box is displayed.

3. In the **Parameter Type** area of this dialog box, ensure that the **Project parameter** radio button is selected.

4. Next, in the **Categories** area, select the **Mechanical** check box from the **Filter list** drop-down list if it is not selected by default. Now, select the **Spaces** check box from the list box displayed below the **Filter list** drop-down list.

5. In the **Parameter Data** area of the dialog box, click in the **Name** edit box and enter the text **Required Illumination Level**. Next, select the **Electrical** option from the **Discipline** drop-down list.

6. Now, select the **Illuminance** and **Electrical-Lighting** options from the **Type of Parameter** and **Group parameter under** drop-down lists, respectively.

7. Next, in the **Parameter Properties** dialog box, ensure that the **Instance** and the **Values are aligned per group type** radio buttons are selected.

8. Choose the **OK** button; the **Parameter Properties** dialog box is closed and the **Project Parameters** dialog box is displayed.

9. In the **Parameters available to elements in this project** area of this dialog box, ensure that the **Required Illumination Level** option is selected and then choose the **OK** button; the **Project Parameters** dialog box is closed.

The new parameter you created applies to all spaces in the project. To verify this, you can look at the properties of one of the spaces

10. Select a space in the project view; the new parameter is displayed under the **Electrical-Lighting** head in the **Properties** palette, as shown in Figure 6-10.

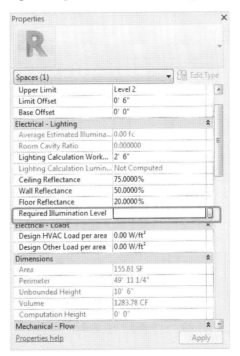

Figure 6-10 *The new parameter added in the* **Properties** *palette of the space*

Creating a Key Schedule for the Required Illuminance Level

You can use the new parameter to enter a value for the illuminance required for each space. However, there are many spaces in this project that have similar lighting requirements, and it is more efficient to create a key schedule and use it to assign the required illuminance values based on the space type. In this section, you will create a key schedule to define the illumination level of each of the space type in the project.

1. Invoke the **Schedule/Quantities** tool from the **Reports & Schedule** panel of the **Analyze** tab; the **New Schedule** dialog box is displayed.

2. In this dialog box, select the **Spaces** option from the **Category** list box and then click in the **Name** edit box and type **Required Illumination-Spaces**.

3. Select the **Schedule keys** radio button and then in the **Key name** edit box, type **Illumination Levels (fc)**.

4. Choose **OK**; the **New Schedule** dialog box is closed and the **Schedule Properties** dialog box is displayed.

5. In the dialog box, ensure that the **Key Name** option is added in the **Scheduled fields (in order)** list box.

   Note
   *In a BIM project, you can use a schedule either as a design interface (Key schedule) or as a documentation tool (Schedule building components). To create a key schedule, select the **Schedule keys** radio button in the **New Schedule** dialog box. Alternatively, in the **New Schedule** dialog box, select the **Schedule building components** radio button to create the schedule of building components.*

6. In the **Schedule Properties** dialog box, ensure that the **Fields** tab is chosen. Now, select the **Required Illumination Level** option from the **Available fields** list box and choose the **Add parameter(s)** button; the **Required Illumination Level** field is added in the **Scheduled fields (in order)** area of the **Schedule Properties** dialog box.

7. Choose **OK**; the dialog box is closed and the **Modify Schedule/Quantities** contextual tab is displayed. Also, the schedule is displayed in the drawing area.

8. Now, drag the borders of the columns in the schedule horizontally to get the desired column width so that the text in the schedules is fully visible.

   Note
   You can double-click on column dividers to auto-fit column width to its content.

Entering the Required Illumination Level Requirements in the Key Schedule

1. Choose the **Insert Data Row** tool from **Modify Schedule/Quantities > Rows** panel; a row is added in the schedule, as shown in Figure 6-11. Similarly, add seven more rows. Refer to Figure 6-12 for the schedule displaying eight rows.

<Required Illumination-Spaces>

A	B
Key Name	Required Illumination Level
1	
2	
3	
4	
5	
6	
7	
8	

Figure 6-12 *All rows added in the schedule*

<Required Illumination-Spaces>

A	B
Key Name	Required Illumination Level
1	

Figure 6-11 *A row added in the schedule*

2. In the schedule displayed in the drawing area, enter the values under the **Key Name** and the **Required Illumination Level** columns, as per the table given next. Refer to Figure 6-13 for viewing the values entered.

Key Name	Required Illumination Level -(fc)
Office-Private	30
Open Office	45
Main Entrance	45
Conference	35
Lounge	25
Restroom	30
Services-Electrical/Mech	20
Circulation	20

<Required Illumination-Spaces>

A	B
Key Name	Required Illumination Level
Circulation	20 fc
Conference	35 fc
Lounge	25 fc
Main Entrance	45 fc
Office-Private	30 fc
Open Office	45 fc
Restroom	30 fc
Services-Electrical/Mech	20 fc

Figure 6-13 *The schedule displaying all the values specified under the **Key Name** Column*

Tip
*The entries in the key schedules are automatically sorted alphabetically by the **Key Name**. However, you can change the sort keys for the added schedule. To do so, select the **Required Illumination-Spaces** schedule from the **Project Browser** and then in the **Properties** palette, edit the **Sorting/Grouping** parameter.*

Assigning the Space Keys to the Spaces

1.   In the **Project Browser**, double-click on the **1-Lighting** node under **Electrical > Lighting > Floor Plans**.

2.   Next, choose the **Tag All** tool from the **Tag** panel of the **Annotate** tab; the **Tag All Not Tagged** dialog box is displayed.

3.   In this dialog box, ensure that the **All objects in current view** radio button is selected. Next, select the **Space Tags** option displayed in the **Category** column and choose **Apply** and then **OK**; the **Tag All Not Tagged** dialog box is closed and the space tags are displayed in the drawing.

4.   In the upper left corner of the floor plan, select the space with the name and number displayed as **CEO-Office** and **101**.

5.   On selecting the space, the properties related to it are displayed in the **Properties** palette.

6.   In the **Properties** palette, click in **Value** field corresponding to the **Illumination Levels (fc)** parameter and select the **Office-Private** option from the drop-down list displayed, as shown in Figure 6-14, and choose **Apply**.

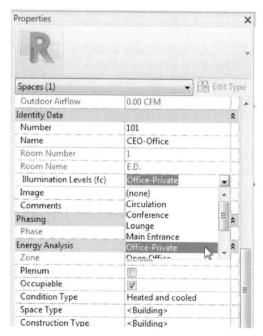

*Figure 6-14 Selecting the **Office-Private** option from the drop-down list*

7.   Now, repeat the procedure followed in step 6 to assign the specified key name for the remaining spaces as per the table given next.

Office Number	Name	Illumination Levels (fc)-Key Name
101	CEO-Office	Office-Private
102	V.P. Marketing	Office-Private
103	Toilet-1	Restroom
104	Rest Room	Restroom
105	Cafeteria	Restroom
106	Store	Services-Electrical/Mech
107	Purchase	Office-Private
108	International	Office-Private
109	H.R.	Office-Private
110	Central Area	Open Office
111	Quality	Office-Private
112	Open	Circulation
113	Conference-2	Conference
114	Conference	Conference
115	Lounge	Lounge
116	Meeting Room	Circulation
117	Service	Services-Electrical/Mech
118	Shaft	Open Office
119	Service-2	Services-Electrical/Mech
120	Accounts	Office-Private
121	Chase	Circulation
122	Electrical	Office-Private
123	Server	Office-Private
124	Store-1	Office-Private
125	Services	Office-Private
126	Toilet-Mens	Restroom
127	Space	Circulation
128	Toilet-C	Restroom
129	Toilet-A	Restroom
130	Toilet-B	Restroom
131	Toilet-Ladies	Restroom

8. Choose the **Modify** button from the **Select** panel to exit the selection.

Assigning Space Color Fills

1. In the **Properties** palette, choose the **<none>** option corresponding to the **Color Scheme** parameter; the **Edit Color Scheme** dialog box is displayed.

2. In the **Schemes** area of the displayed dialog box, ensure that the **Spaces** option is selected from the **Category** drop-down list. Next, in the list box displayed in the **Schemes** area, select the **Schema 1** option; various options for editing the schema are displayed in the **Scheme Definition** area.

3. In the **Scheme Definition** area, enter **Lighting Analysis** in the **Title** edit box. In this area, select the **Required Illumination Level** option from the **Color** drop-down list; the **Colors Not Preserved** window is displayed, as shown in Figure 6-15.

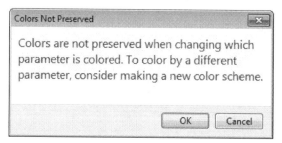

*Figure 6-15 The **Colors Not Preserved** window*

4. In this window, choose **OK**; the window is closed and the default color scheme is displayed in a table in the **Edit Color Scheme** dialog box.

5. In the **Scheme Definition** area, select the **By range** radio button and then select the first cell in the second row; the **Add Value** button (+ icon) is displayed on the left of the table. Choose the **Add Value** button twice; two rows will be added below the selected cell, as shown in Figure 6-16.

6. Choose **Apply** and then **OK**; the **Edit Color Scheme** dialog box is closed and the color scheme is applied in the drawing.

7. Next, choose the **Color Fill Legend** tool from the **Color Fill** panel in the **Annotate** tab; the legend is displayed along with the cursor.

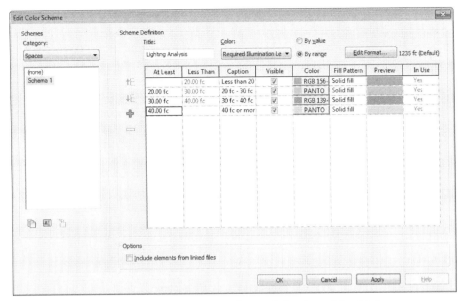

Figure 6-16 The **Edit Color Scheme** *dialog box with added rows*

8. In the drawing area, click at a suitable point near the floor plan; the legend is displayed. Refer to Figure 6-17 for the color scheme applied to the project view and the inserted legend.

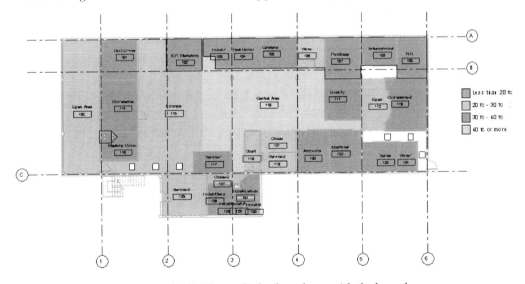

Figure 6-17 The applied color scheme with the legend

Comparing the Illumination Level

1. Choose the **Schedule/Quantities** tool from the **Reports & Schedules** panel of the **Analyze** tab; the **New Schedule** dialog box is displayed.

2. In this dialog box, select the **Spaces** option from the **Category** list box and then in the **Name** edit box, enter **Lighting Analysis**.

3. Ensure that the **Schedule building components** radio button is selected and then choose **OK**; the **Schedule Properties** dialog box is displayed.

4. In this dialog box, ensure that the **Fields** tab is chosen by default and then in the **Available fields** area, click on the **Name** option. Now, press and hold the CTRL key and select the following fields: **Number**, **Required Illumination Level**, **Average Estimated Illumination**, **Ceiling Reflectance**, **Wall Reflectance**, **Floor Reflectance**, and **Lighting Calculation Workplane**.

5. Choose the **Add parameter(s)** button; the selected fields are added in the **Schedule fields (in order)** area, as shown in Figure 6-18.

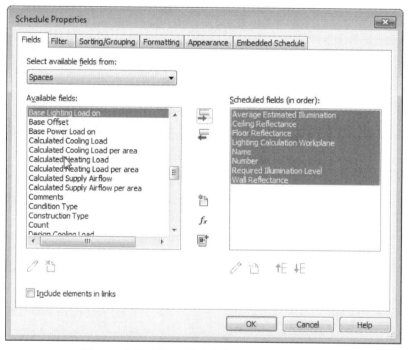

*Figure 6-18 The added fields in the **Fields** tab*

6. Next, choose the **Add calculated parameter** button; the **Calculated Value** dialog box is displayed. In this dialog box, enter **Delta** in the **Name** edit box and then select the **Formula** radio button if it is not selected by default.

7. In the **Calculated Value** dialog box, select the **Electrical** and the **Illuminance** options from the **Discipline** and **Type** drop-down lists, respectively.

8. Now, choose the browse button next to the **Formula** edit box; the **Fields** dialog box is displayed. In the displayed dialog box, select the **Average Estimated Illumination** option from the **Select the field to be added to the formula** list box and then choose **OK**; the **Fields** dialog box is closed and the selected field is displayed in the **Formula** edit box.

9.   Now, in the **Formula** edit box, add the "**-**" symbol after the text **Average Estimated Illumination** and then again choose the browse button next to the edit box; the **Fields** dialog box is displayed.

10. In the **Select the field to be added to the formula** list box of the dialog box, select the **Required Illumination Level** option and choose **OK**; the **Fields** dialog box is closed and the formula **Average Estimated Illumination-Required Illumination Level** is displayed in the **Formula** edit box.

11. Choose **OK**; the **Calculated Value** dialog box is closed and the **Schedule Properties** dialog box is displayed.

12. In the **Schedule Properties** dialog box, notice that the **Delta** field is added in the **Schedule Fields (in order)** area and then choose the **Sorting/Grouping** tab.

13. In this tab, select the **Number** option from the **Sort by** drop-down list and ensure that the **Ascending** radio button and the **Itemize every instance** check box are selected.

14. Now, choose the **Formatting** tab in the **Schedule Properties** dialog box and then in the **Fields** area, select the **Delta** value; the formatting options for this field are displayed in the right pane; as shown in Figure 6-19.

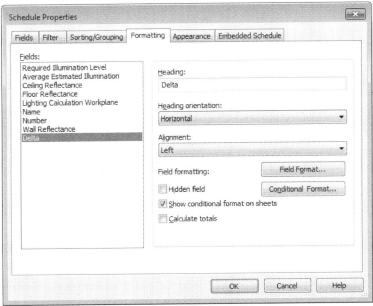

*Figure 6-19 The formatting options for the **Delta** field*

15   Next, choose the **Conditional Format** button; the **Conditional Formatting** dialog box for the selected field is displayed.

16. In this dialog box, select the **Not Between** option from the **Test** drop-down list and then in the **Value** area, enter **-10 fc** and **10 fc** in the left and right edit boxes displayed. On entering the values, the text **-10.00 fc > Delta or Delta > 10.00 fc** is displayed in the **Conditions to Use** text box, refer to Figure 6-20.

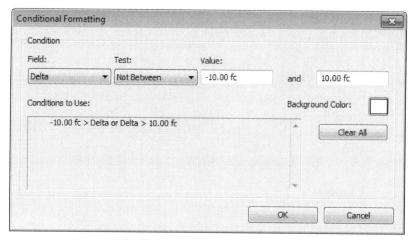

*Figure 6-20 The **Conditional Formatting** dialog box*

17. In the **Conditional Formatting** dialog box, choose the **Background Color** swatch; the **Color** dialog box is displayed.

18. In the **Color** dialog box, enter the values in the specified edit boxes as given next.

       Red: **128**   Green: **64**   Blue: **64**

19. Next, choose **OK** twice; the **Color** and the **Conditional Formatting** dialog boxes are closed. And, the **Schedule Properties** dialog box with the **Formatting** tab chosen is displayed.

20. Next, in the **Schedule Properties** dialog box, select the **Ceiling Reflectance** option from the **Fields** list box and then choose the **Field Format** button; the **Format** dialog box is displayed.

21. In this dialog box, clear the **Use project settings** check box and then select the **Fixed** option from the **Units** drop-down list.

22. Next, ensure that the **2 decimals places** option is selected in the **Rounding** drop-down list and then choose **OK**; the **Format** dialog box is closed.

23. Next, repeat the procedure as explained in steps 21 and 22 for the **Wall Reflectance** and **Floor Reflectance** options.

24. After assigning the field formatting values for the specified fields, choose **OK**; the **Schedule Properties** dialog box is closed and the **<Lighting Analysis>** schedule is displayed in the drawing window, as shown in Figure 6-21.

<Lighting Analysis>

A	B	C	D	E	F	G	H	I
Required Illuminati	Average Estimated Illumination	Ceiling Reflectanc	Floor Reflectance	Lighting Calculatio	Name	Number	Wall Reflectance	Delta
30 fc	15 fc	0.75	20.00%	2'-6"	CEO-Office	101	0.50	15.07 fc
30 fc	0 fc	0.75	20.00%	2'-6"	V.P. Marketing	102	0.50	30.20 fc
30 fc	0 fc	0.75	20.00%	2'-6"	Toilet-1	103	0.50	30.00 fc
30 fc	0 fc	0.75	20.00%	2'-6"	Rest Room	104	0.50	30.00 fc
30 fc	0 fc	0.75	20.00%	2'-6"	Cafeteria	105	0.50	30.00 fc
20 fc	0 fc	0.75	20.00%	2'-6"	Store	106	0.50	20.00 fc
30 fc	0 fc	0.75	20.00%	2'-6"	Purchase	107	0.50	30.00 fc
30 fc	0 fc	0.75	20.00%	2'-6"	International	108	0.50	30.00 fc
30 fc	0 fc	0.75	20.00%	2'-6"	H.R.	109	0.50	30.00 fc
45 fc	0 fc	0.75	20.00%	2'-6"	Central Area	110	0.50	45.00 fc
30 fc	0 fc	0.75	20.00%	2'-6"	Quality	111	0.50	30.00 fc
20 fc	0 fc	0.75	20.00%	2'-6"	Open	112	0.50	20.00 fc
35 fc	0 fc	0.75	20.00%	2'-6"	Conference-2	113	0.50	35.00 fc
35 fc	0 fc	0.75	20.00%	2'-6"	Conference	114	0.50	35.00 fc
25 fc	0 fc	0.75	20.00%	2'-6"	Lounge	115	0.50	25.00 fc
35 fc	0 fc	0.75	20.00%	2'-6"	Meeting Room	116	0.50	35.00 fc
30 fc	0 fc	0.75	20.00%	2'-6"	Service-1	117	0.50	30.00 fc
20 fc	0 fc	0.75	20.00%	2'-6"	Shaft	118	0.50	20.00 fc
20 fc	0 fc	0.75	20.00%	2'-6"	Service-2	119	0.50	20.00 fc
30 fc	0 fc	0.75	20.00%	2'-6"	Accounts	120	0.50	30.00 fc
20 fc	0 fc	0.75	20.00%	2'-6"	Chase	121	0.50	20.00 fc
30 fc	0 fc	0.75	20.00%	2'-6"	Electrical	122	0.50	30.00 fc
30 fc	0 fc	0.75	20.00%	2'-6"	Server	123	0.50	30.00 fc
30 fc	0 fc	0.75	20.00%	2'-6"	Store-1	124	0.50	30.00 fc

*Figure 6-21 The **Lighting Analysis** schedule displaying different illumination levels*

Note
*The created schedule displays the value of **Average Estimated Illumination Level** for all the spaces as **0**. This is because you have not yet added lighting fixtures to any of the spaces. Also, notice that the **Delta** has been calculated for each of the occupied spaces, and in every case, the value in the **Delta** column is highlighted. This is because the value is not within the +/-10 fc range that you specified in the **Conditional Formatting** dialog box.*

Saving and Closing the Project
In this section, you need to save the project and the settings using the **Save As** tool.

1. Choose **Save As > Project** from **File Menu**. As you are saving the project for the first time, the **Save As** dialog box is displayed.

2. In this dialog box, browse to the *C:\rmp_2019\c06_rmp_2019_tut* folder and then in the **File name** edit box, enter the text **c06_Office-Space_tut2** (for Metric **M_c06_Office-Space_tut2**) and then choose the **Save** button to save the current project file with the specified name and to close the **Save As** dialog box.

3. To close the project, choose the **Close** option from **File** menu.

EXERCISE
Exercise 1   Placing Lighting Fixtures and Switches

Download the *c06_Conference-Center_exer1.rvt* file (for Metric *M_c06_Conference-Center_exer1.rvt*) from *http://www.cadsofttech.com*. The path of the file is as follows: *Textbooks > Civil/GIS > Revit MEP > Revit MEP 2019 for Novices*.

In this exercise, you will add the lighting fixtures, switches, and junction boxes for spaces in the 1ST Floor-ELEC LIGHT'G view. Refer to Figure 6-22 for the placement of various components.

1. Project view to be used:
   > Floor Plans > Electrical > 1ST Floor-ELEC LIGHT'G

2. Family type to be used:
   Lighting Fixtures
	For Imperial	Duplex Receptacle: Standard and M_Duplex Receptacle: GFCI
	For Metric	M_Duplex Receptacle: Standard and M_Duplex Receptacle: GFCI

   Switches
	For Imperial	Lighting Switches: Single Pole
	For Metric	M_ Lighting Switches: Single Pole

   Junction Boxes
	For Imperial	Junction Boxes-Load: 4" Square 120-1
	For Metric	M_Junction Boxes-Load: 4" Square 120-1

3. Elevation
Switches:	3' 9" (1145mm)
Receptacles:	1'3" (381mm)
Junction Boxes:	8' (2438mm)

4. File name to be assigned: *c06_Conference-Center_exer1a.rvt* (for Metric *M_ c06_ Conference-Center_exer1a.rvt*)

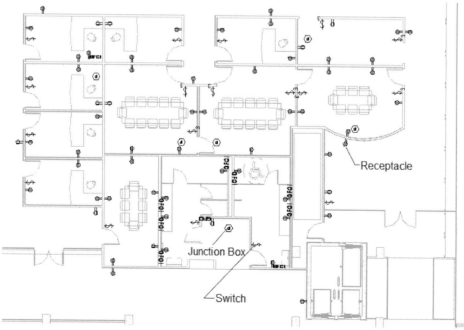

Figure 6-22 *The placement of various electrical components in the project*

Chapter 7

Creating Plumbing Systems

Learning Objectives

After completing this chapter, you will be able to:

- *Add plumbing fixtures*
- *Create pipe settings*
- *Auto route the pipe*
- *Manually route the pipe*

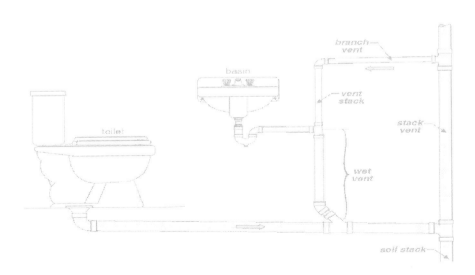

INTRODUCTION

A plumbing system is a network of pipes, drain fittings, valves, valve assemblies, and devices that are installed in a building to distribute water for drinking, washing, and heating, and also to drain the waste out of the building. In this chapter, you will learn various steps involved in creating a plumbing system in a building.

CREATING A PLUMBING SYSTEM

To create a plumbing system in Revit, you will need to add plumbing fixtures, define various pipe settings, and then route the pipe to connect the fixtures to supply water or drain the waste out of it. Figure 7-1 shows a typical plumbing system in a building. In Revit, you can create the plumbing system under the **Plumbing** discipline. To start working in a plumbing system, expand **Plumbing > Floor Plans** node in the **Project Browser** and then click on the desired level. In the **Project Browser**, the following floor plans are available under the **Floor Plans** node: **1-Plumbing** and **2-Plumbing**. You can select any of these floor plans and start creating the plumbing system. The steps involved in creating a plumbing system are as follows.

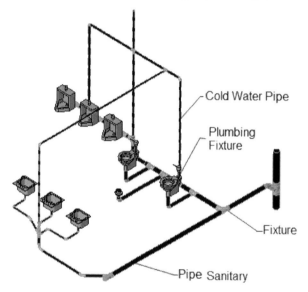

Figure 7-1 A typical plumbing system in a building project

Adding Plumbing Fixtures
Specifying the Pipe Settings
Routing Pipes in the Pipe System
Modifying a Pipe Segment
Placing Fittings
Placing Pipe Accessories

TUTORIAL
General instructions for downloading tutorial files:

1. Download the *c07_rmp_2019_tut.zip* file for this tutorial from http://www.cadsoftech.com. The path of the file is as follows: *Textbooks > Civil/GIS > Revit MEP > Revit MEP 2019 for Novices.*

2. Now, save and extract the downloaded folder at the following location: *C:\rmp_2019*

 Note
The default unit system used in the tutorials is Imperial.

Tutorial 1   Office-Space

In this tutorial, you will create a plumbing system for the Office-Space project with the following parameters and project specifications: **(Expected time: 45 min)**

1. File name to be used:
   - For Imperial   *c07_Office-Space_tut1.rvt*
   - For Metric   *M_c07_Office-Space_tut1.rvt*
2. File name to be assigned:
   - For Imperial   *c07_Office-Space_tut1a.rvt*
   - For Metric   *M_c07_Office-Space_tut1a.rvt*

The following steps are required to complete this tutorial:

a. Open the project file
b. Load the plumbing component families.
c. Configure the piping systems.
d. Adding the plumbing fixtures.
e. Set the view range.
f. Place the floor drain.
g. Create the sanitary system.
h. View the plumbing system in 3D.
i. Save the project by using the **Save As** tool.
   - For Imperial   *c07_Office-Space_tut1a.rvt*
   - For Metric   *M_c07_Office-Space_tut1a.rvt*
j. Close the project by using the **Close** tool.

Opening a Project

1. Choose **Open > Project** from the **File** menu; the **Open** dialog box is displayed.

2. In the **Open** dialog box, browse to *C:\rmp_2019\c07_rmp_2019_tut* and select the desired file.
   - For Imperial   *c07_Office-Space_tut1*
   - For Metric   *M_c07_Office-Space_tut1*

3. Now, choose **Open**; the selected file opens in the Revit interface.

Loading the Plumbing Component Families

1. Choose the **Load Family** tool from the **Load from Library** panel of the **Insert** tab; the **Load Family** dialog box is displayed.

2. In this dialog box, browse to **US Imperial > Plumbing > MEP > Fixtures > Urinals** folder and then select the **Urinal - Wall Hung.rfa** file and choose **Open**; the selected family is loaded in the current project. For the Metric system, browse to **US Metric > Plumbing > MEP > Fixtures > Urinals** folder and then select the **M_Urinal - Wall Hung.rfa** file.

3. Repeat the procedure followed in steps 1 and 2 and select the other family files required for this tutorial from their respective folders. Refer to the table given next for the name of the files and their folder location.

Name of the Family Catagory(ies)	Folder Location (Imperial)	Folder Location (Metric)
Water Closet - Flush Valve - Floor Mounted (Imperial) M_Water Closet - Flush Valve - Floor Mounted (Metric)	US Imperial > Plumbing > MEP > Fixtures > Water Closets	US Metric > Plumbing > MEP > Fixtures > Water Closets
Sink - Island - Single.rfa (Imperial) M_Sink - Island - Single. rfa (Metric)`	US Imperial > Plumbing > MEP > Fixtures > Sinks	US Metric > Plumbing > MEP > Fixtures > Sinks
Floor Drain - Round(Imperial) M_Floor Drain - Round (Metric)	US Imperial > Plumbing > MEP > Fixtures > Drains	US Metric > Plumbing > MEP > Fixtures > Drains
Tee - PVC - Sch 40 (Imperial) M_Tee - PVC - Sch 40 (Metric)	US Imperial > Pipe > Fittings > PVC > Sch 40 > Socket-Type	US Metric > Pipe > Fittings > PVC > Sch 40 > Socket-Type
Bend - PVC - Sch 40 - DWV (Imperial) M_Bend - PVC - Sch 40 - DWV (Metric)	US Imperial > Pipe > Fittings > PVC > Sch 40 > Socket-Type > DWV	US Metric > Pipe > Fittings > PVC > Sch 40 > Socket-Type > DWV

Note

*In case, the families are already present in the project, the **Family Already Exists** dialog box is displayed. Choose the **Overwrite the existing version and its parameter values** option; the family is loaded.*

Configuring the Piping Systems

1. In the **Project Browser**, double-click on the **PVC-DWV** sub-node from **Families > Pipes > Pipe Types** node; the **Type Properties** dialog box is displayed.

2. In this dialog box, choose the **Duplicate** button; the **Name** dialog box is displayed.

3. In this dialog box, type the **Sanitary-PVC** text in the **Name** edit box.

4. Choose **OK**; the **Name** dialog box is closed and the **Type Properties** dialog box appears.

5. In the **Type Properties** dialog box, ensure that the **Sanitary-PVC** option is selected in the **Type** drop-down list and then choose the **Edit** button displayed in the **Value** field corresponding to the **Routing Preferences** parameter; the **Routing Preferences** dialog box is displayed.

6. In this dialog box, click in the desired field and select the required options from the drop-down list displayed. The options to be selected are given in Figure 7-2.

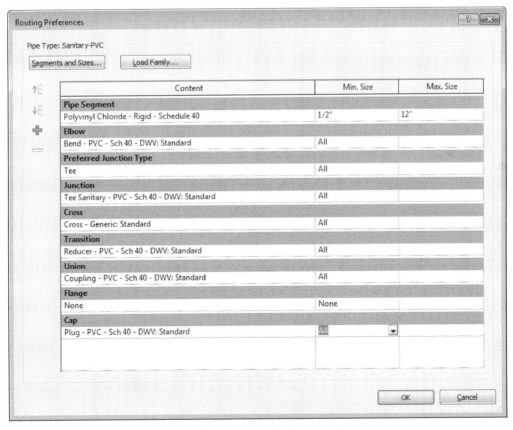

*Figure 7-2 The **Routing Preferences** dialog box*

7. After assigning the specified values in the **Routing Preferences** dialog box, choose **OK** to close it.

8. In the **Type Properties** dialog box, again choose the **Duplicate** button; the **Name** dialog box is displayed. In this dialog box, type **Sanitary Vent-PVC** in the **Name** edit box and choose **OK**; the **Name** dialog box is closed.

9. In the **Type Properties** dialog box, ensure that the **Sanitary Vent-PVC** option is selected by default and then choose the **Edit** button corresponding to the **Routing Preference** parameter; the **Routing Preferences** dialog box is displayed.

10. In this dialog box, choose the **Load Family** button; the **Load Family** dialog box is displayed.

11. In the **Load Family** dialog box, browse to **US Imperial > Pipe > Fittings > PVC > Sch 40 > Socket-Type > DWV** folder and then select the **Tee Vent - PVC - Sch 40 - DWV** family from the list. For Metric system, browse to **US Metric > Pipe > Fittings > PVC > Sch 40 > Socket-Type > DWV** folder and then select the **M_Tee Vent - PVC - Sch 40 - DWV** family from the list. Choose **Open**; the **Load Family** dialog box is closed. In the **Content** column of the **Routing Preferences** dialog box, click on the field corresponding to the **Junction** option and select the **Tee-Vent PVC - Sch 40 - DWV: Standard** option for Imperial or **M_Tee Vent - PVC - Sch 40 - DWV : Standard** for Metric from the drop-down list displayed.

12. Keep rest of the settings unchanged in the **Routing Preferences** dialog box, refer to Figure 7-2 and choose the **OK** button; the **Routing Preferences** dialog box is closed.

13. In the **Type Properties** dialog box, choose **OK** to close it.

Adding the Plumbing Fixtures

In this section, you need to add 1 toilet, 2 urinals, 2 sinks, and a floor drain to the floor plan of the Office-Space project.

1. Choose the **Plumbing Fixture** tool from the **Plumbing & Piping** panel of the **Systems** tab; the **Modify | Place Plumbing Fixture** contextual tab is displayed. In this tab, choose the **Tag on Placement** button from the **Tag** panel, if it is not chosen by default. This enables the placing of the tag along with the fixture.

2. In the **Properties** palette, select the **Water Closet-Flush Valve -Floor Mounted Private-1.6 gpf** option from the **Type Selector** drop-down list. For Metric system, select **M_Water Closet-Flush Valve -Floor Mounted Private-6.1 Lpf**.

3. In the **Options Bar**, select the **Rotate after placement** check box.

4. Next, zoom in the toilet area in the south. Now, move the cursor inside the toilet area and click at the location shown in Figure 7-3.

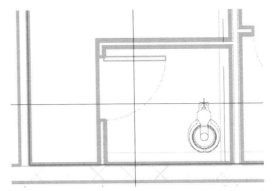

Figure 7-3 *The fixture placed at the specified location*

5. Next, in the **Options Bar**, enter **-90** in the **Angle** edit box and press ENTER; the fixture is placed at the specified location, as shown in Figure 7-4.

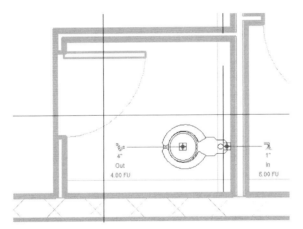

Figure 7-4 *The fixture placed after rotation*

6. Choose **Modify** from the **Select** panel to exit the **Plumbing Fixture** tool.

7. Next, choose the **Plumbing Fixture** tool from the **Plumbing & Piping** panel of the **Systems** tab; the **Modify | Place Plumbing Fixture** contextual tab is displayed.

8. In the **Properties** palette, select the **Urinal Wall Hung 3/4" Flush Valve** from the **Type Selector** drop-down list. Also, click in the value field of the **Elevation** parameter and type **1'6"**. For Metric system, select the **Urinal Wall Hung 20 mm Flush Valve** from the **Type Selector** drop-down list. Then, in the **Properties** palette, click in the value field of the **Elevation** parameter and type **450**.

9. In the **Properties** palette, ensure that the **Level 1** option is specified corresponding to the **Schedule Level** parameter.

10. Now, in the **Placement** panel of the **Modify | Place Plumbing Fixture** contextual tab, ensure that the **Place on Vertical Face** button is chosen. Next, place the cursor at a location in the toilet area, as shown in Figure 7-5. Click to place the fixture at the specified location.

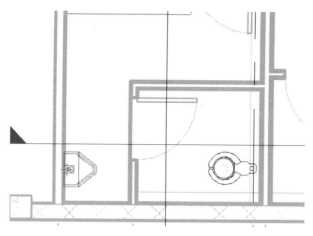

Figure 7-5 *The urinal fixture placed at the desired location*

11. Repeat the procedure given in step 10 to place another urinal of the same type, as shown in Figure 7-6.

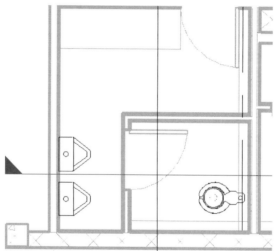

Figure 7-6 *The second urinal fixture placed at the specified location*

12. After placing the urinals, choose the **Modify** tool to exit the selection.

13. Choose the **Plumbing Fixture** tool from the **Plumbing & Piping** panel of the **Systems** tab; the **Modify | Place Plumbing Fixture** contextual tab is displayed.

14. In the **Properties** palette, select the **Sink-Island-Single 18"x18"-Private** type from the **Type Selector** drop-down list. For Metric system, select the **M_Sink-Island-Single 455 x455mm-Private** type.

15. Now, choose the **Place on Face** tool from the **Placement** panel of the **Modify | Place Plumbing Fixture** contextual tab.

16. Move the cursor at the face of the slab and click, refer to Figure 7-7; the sink is placed.

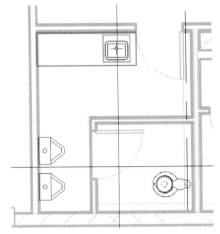

Figure 7-7 The preview of the sink fixture displayed

17. Add one more sink as done in previous steps. For placing the sink, refer to Figure 7-8.

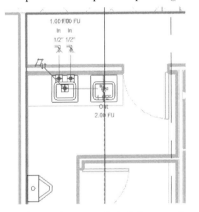

Figure 7-8 The second sink fixture placed

18. Choose **Modify** from the **Select** panel of the **Modify| Place Plumbing Fixture** contextual tab.

Setting the View Range

In this section, you will set the view range of the floor plan view.

1. In the **Properties** palette, choose the **Edit** button corresponding to the **View Range** parameter; the **View Range** dialog box is displayed.

2. In the **Primary Range** area of this dialog box, ensure that the **Associated Level (Level1)** option is selected in the **Bottom** drop-down list and enter **-5' (-1500 mm)** in the **Offset** edit box displayed next to it.

3.   In the **View Depth** area of this dialog box, ensure that the **Associated Level (Level1)** option is selected in the **Level** drop-down list and then enter **-5' (-1500 mm)** in the **Offset** edit box displayed next to it.

4.   Choose **Apply** and then **OK** to close the **View Range** dialog box.

Placing the Floor Drain

In this section, you will place the floor drain in the view.

1.   Choose the **Plumbing Fixture** tool from the **Plumbing & Piping** panel of the **Systems** tab; the **Modify | Place Plumbing Fixture** contextual tab is displayed.

2.   In the **Properties** palette, select the **Floor Drain - Round: 5" Strainer - 2" Drain** from the **Type Selector** drop-down list. For Metric system, select the **Floor Drain - Round: 125mm Strainer - 50mm Drain** option.

3.   Choose the **Place on Face** tool from the **Placement** panel and then move the cursor to the location shown in Figure 7-9, and click; the floor drain is placed.

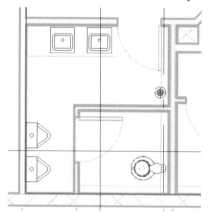

Figure 7-9 The location of the floor drain

4.   Now, choose the **Modify** button from the **Select** panel to exit the **Plumbing Fixture** tool.

Creating the Sanitary System

1.   Choose the **Analyze** tab and then choose the **Show Disconnects** button from the **Check Systems** panel; the **Show Disconnects Options** dialog box is displayed.

2.   In this dialog box, select the **Pipe** check box and choose the **OK** button; the **Show Disconnects Options** dialog box is closed and all the open connectors in the fixtures are displayed as warning symbols.

3.   Choose the **Visual Style** button in the **View Control Bar** and then choose the **Wireframe** option from the flyout displayed.

4. Choose the **Mechanical Settings** button from the **Plumbing & Piping** panel of the **Systems** tab; the **Mechanical Settings** dialog box is displayed.

5. In the left-pane of this dialog box, choose **Pipe Settings > Conversions**; the right-pane displays various properties related to the pipe settings, refer to Figure 7-10.

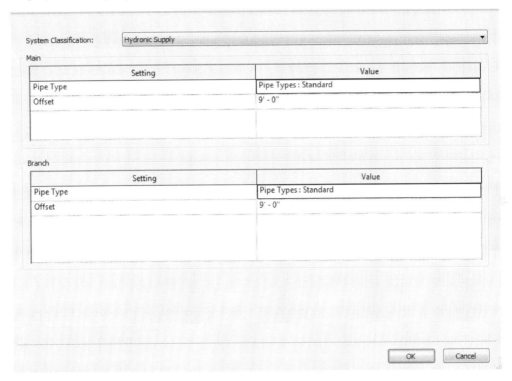

Figure 7-10 *Various properties displayed related to pipe settings*

6. In the right pane, select the **Sanitary** option from the **System Classification** drop-down list.

7. In the **Main** area, click in the **Value** field corresponding to the **Pipe Type** parameter and select the **Pipe Types : PVC - DWV** option from the drop-down list displayed.

8. Specify the other settings in the **Main** and **Branch** areas, as shown in Figure 7-11. For Metric system, specify **-305** for the **Offset** parameters.

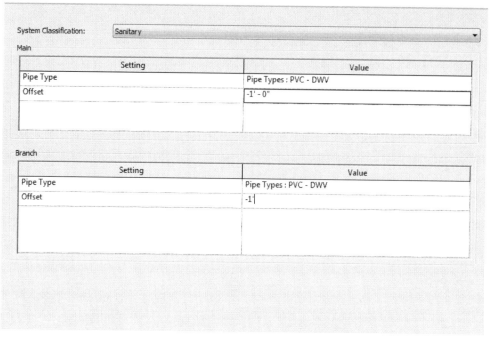

*Figure 7-11 The pipe settings for the **Sanitary** system*

9. Choose **OK**; the **Mechanical Settings** dialog box is closed.

10. Select the water closet and the floor drain fixtures, as shown in Figure 7-12; the **Modify |
    Plumbing Fixtures** tab is displayed.

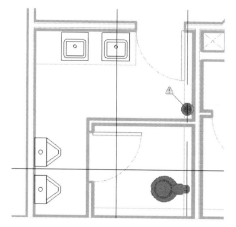

*Figure 7-12 The floor drain and the water
closet fixtures selected*

11. In the **Create Systems** panel, choose the **Piping** tool; the **Create Piping System** dialog box
    is displayed.

12. In this dialog box, ensure that the **Sanitary** option is selected in the **System** type drop-down list.

13. In the **System name** edit box, type **Drainage System -Toilet 1** and choose **OK**; the fixtures in the system are bounded in a rectangular box, as shown in Figure 7-13.

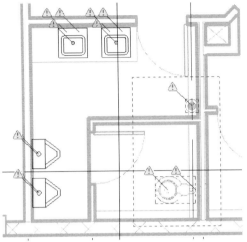

Figure 7-13 *The fixtures in the system bounded in a rectangular box*

14. Choose the **Generate Layout** tool from the **Layout** panel; the **Generate Layout** contextual tab is displayed.

15. In the **Options Bar**, ensure that the **Network** option is selected in the **Solution Type** drop-down list and then choose the **Next Solution** button, "**>**"; the text **2 of 5** is displayed before it and a solution is displayed in the drawing, as shown in Figure 7-14.

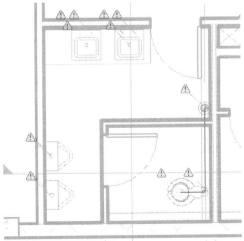

Figure 7-14 *The layout solution for the system*

16. In the **Options Bar**, choose the **Settings** button; the **Pipe Conversion Settings** dialog box is displayed.

17. In the left pane of this dialog box, ensure that the **Main** option is selected and then in the right pane, enter **-1'** (**-305 mm**) in the **Offset** parameter. Next, select the **Pipe Types: PVC - DWV** option in the **Pipe Type** parameter.

18. In the left pane of the **Pipe Conversion Settings** dialog box, select the **Branch** option. In the right pane, enter **-1'** (**-305 mm**) for the **Offset** parameter and select **Pipe Types: PVC - DWV** for the **Pipe Type** parameter.

19. Choose **OK**; the **Pipe Conversion Settings** dialog box is closed.

20. Choose the **Finish Layout** tool from the **Generate Layout** panel of the **Generate Layout** tab; the pipe system is created between the fixtures. Now, choose the **Detail Level** option in the **View Control Bar**; a flyout is displayed. Select the **Fine** option from the displayed flyout.

21. Next, select the floor drain fixture and then choose the **Piping Systems** tab; the options in this tab are displayed.

22. In the **Piping Systems** tab, ensure that the **Drainage System-Toilet 1** option is selected in the **System Selector** drop-down list in the **System Tools** panel and then choose the **Edit System** tool; the **Edit Piping System** contextual tab is displayed.

23. In this tab, ensure that the **Add to System** button is chosen in the **Edit Piping System** panel and then select the two urinals and sinks, refer to Figure 7-15.

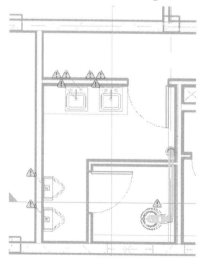

Figure 7-15 *The two urnials and sinks selected*

24. Choose the **Finish Editing System** tool from the **Mode** panel; the urinals and the sinks are added to the system.

25. Next, select any of the two urinals added to the system and then choose the **Generate Layout** tool from the **Layout** panel of the **Modify | Plumbing Fixture** tab; the default layout is displayed in the drawing area.

26. In the **Options Bar**, ensure that the **Network** option is selected in the **Solution Type** drop-down list and the choose the **Next Solution** button three times; the text **4 of 5** is displayed before the button and the solution layout is displayed in the drawing area, as shown in Figure 7-16.

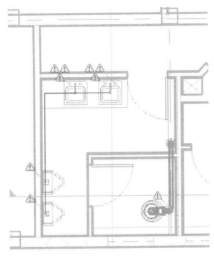

Figure 7-16 *The solution layout of the added fixture*

27. Choose the **Finish Layout** tool from the **Generate Layout** panel of the **Generate Layout** tab; the layout is generated.

Viewing the Plumbing System in 3D

In this section, you will display the 3D view of the plumbing system.

1. Choose the **Manage Links** tool from the **Manage Project** panel of the **Manage** tab; the **Manage Links** dialog box is displayed.

2. In this dialog box, select the **c07_ archi_ plumbing_tut1** option for Imperial (**M_c07_ archi_ plumbing_tut1** option for Metric) in the **Linked Name** column and then choose the **Unload** button; the **Unload Link** dialog box is displayed.

3. Choose the **OK** button; the dialog box is closed.

4. Choose **OK** in the **Manage Links** dialog box to close it.

5. Choose the **Default 3D View** tool from **View > Create > 3D View** drop-down; the 3D view of the system is displayed, as shown in Figure 7-17.

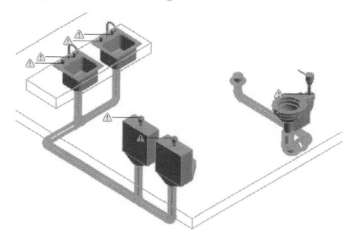

Figure 7-17 *The 3D view of the plumbing system*

Saving the Project

In this section, you need to save the project and the settings using the **Save As** tool.

1. Choose **Save As > Project** from the **File** menu; the **Save As** dialog box is displayed.

2. In this dialog box, browse to *C:\rmp_2019\ c07* folder. Next, in the **File name** edit box, enter the text **c07_Office-Space_tut1** for Imperial or **M_c07_Office-Space_tut1** for Metric and then choose the **Options** button; the **File Save Options** dialog box is displayed.

3. Now, choose the **OK** button; the **File Save Options** dialog box is closed and the **Save As** dialog box appears.
4. In the dialog box, choose the **Save** button; the current project file is saved with the specified name and the **Save As** dialog box is closed.

Closing the Project

1. Choose the **Close** option from **File Menu**; the file is closed and this completes the tutorial.

EXERCISE

Exercise 1   Community Center

Download the *c07_Community-Center_exer1.rvt* file for Imperial or *M_c07_Community-Center_exer1. rvt* file for Metric from *www.cadsofttech.com*. Create a sanitary system for the *Community-Center* project with the following parameters and project specifications. Figures 7-18 and 7-19 show sanitary system.

(Expected time: 1hr)

1. Project View used for creating the plumbing system:
   Floor Plans > Mechanical >1ST FLOOR- PLUMBING
2. Families to be used:
   For Imperial   **Sink-Vanity Round 19"x19"**
   Toilet-Commercial-Wall-3D 15" Seat Height
   Urinal-Wall-3D
   For Metric   **M_Sink-Vanity Round 482 x 482 mm**
   Toilet-Commercial-Wall-3D 380mm Seat Height
   Urinal-Wall-3D
3. Pipe Types: PVC
4. Offset Values:
   Main Pipe   **-1'(-305mm)**
   Branch Pipe   **-1'(-305mm)**
5. File name to be assigned:
   For Imperial   *c07_Community-Center_exer1.rvt*
   For Metric   *M_c07_Community-Center_exer1.rvt*

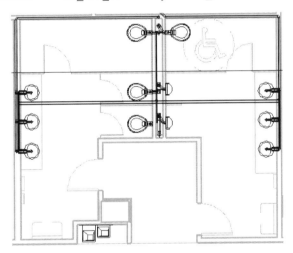

Figure 7-18 *Sanitary System*

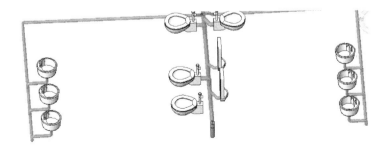

Figure 7-19 *The 3D view of a sanitary system*

This page is intenionally left blank

Chapter 8

Creating Fire Protection System

Learning Objectives

After completing this chapter, you will be able to:
- *Set up the fire protection system project*
- *Create space schedules*
- *Place sprinklers*

INTRODUCTION

Fire Protection or Fire Suppression is one of the major areas for a building design in a project. While designing a Fire Protection System for a project, the designer will use variety of methods and techniques. For example, for designing the schema of a fire protection plan, the designer should plan all the equipment required for the system. This will help in making the fire protection system more efficient and will also improve the coordination between other disciplines. A Fire Protection System consists of the following essential features: fire detection alarm, all types of fixed extinguishing systems, portable systems, private fire main and hydrants, pumping stations, smoke and heat evacuation system, centralized control system, auxiliary equipment, automotive and fire prevention system.

In this chapter, you will learn how to place fire protection equipment, create a wet fire protection system, create a dry protection system, and more.

FIRE PROTECTION SYSTEMS

A fire protection system comprises of sprinklers, pipes, and valves. In Revit, you can create a sprinkler system by placing sprinkler heads, such as upright and pendent as elements. These elements can be placed as hosted in the ceiling or as non-hosted elements. You can then connect the sprinklers with the pipes using the auto layout tools or by manually drawing the pipes. Further, you can check the fire protection system and its components for interferences with other components in a building. Figure 8-1 displays the 3d view of a fire protection system in an MEP project. The information stored within the system can be used for analysis or scheduling purposes. The various features and processes required for creating a fire protection system are discussed next.

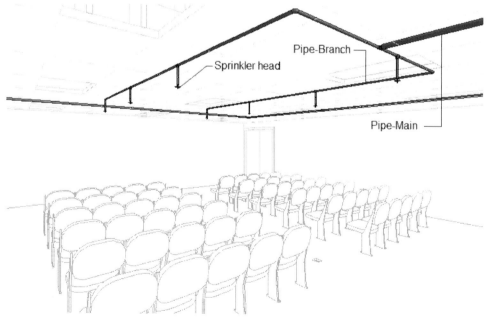

Figure 8-1 Pictorial view of an auditorium with the Fire Protection System installed

Guidelines for Creating a Fire Protection System

To create an efficient fire protection system, following are the recommended guidelines:

1. It is recommended to always place the sprinkler piping above the pendent type sprinkler heads and below the upright sprinkler heads. This is because a piping run in the opposite direction will not connect to the sprinkler as intended.

2. It is recommended to set an elevation for the piping head while using layout tools. This is because the layout tools will not find a solution for piping at an elevation above the upright heads or below the pendent sprinklers.

3. It is recommended not to define the size of sprinklers based on the flow information of individual sprinkler heads. This information is for scheduling, coordination, and analysis purposes only.

DESIGNING THE FIRE PROTECTION SYSTEM

In Revit, you can design both wet and dry fire protection systems. The designing of a fire protection system involves the following steps: setting up the fire protection system, creating the space schedule, placing sprinkler heads, and then connecting the sprinklers. To perform these steps, you need to create different views and pipe types, insert fittings, modify the pipes and fittings manually, create schedules, and size and tag the pipes. In the next sections, the steps involved in designing a fire protection system are discussed next.

Tip
While designing a fire protection system for a building, the following elements are considered critical: Water Supply in the building or site. Occupancy of the building (light hazard, ordinary hazard, extra hazard), and Building Construction

Setting Up a Fire Protection System Project
Creating the Space Schedule
Placing Sprinkler Heads

TUTORIAL

General instructions for downloading tutorial files:

1. Download the *c08_tutorial.zip* file for this tutorial from *http://www.cadsofttech.com*. The path of the folder is as follows: *Textbooks > Civil/GIS > Revit MEP > Revit MEP 2019 For Novices*.

2. Now, save and extract the downloaded zip file at the following location:
   C:\rmp_2019\c08_rmp_2019_tut

Tutorial 1   Office Space- Fire Suppression

In this tutorial, you will create pipe types for dry and wet fire protection. Also, you will create a space schedule to estimate the quantity of sprinklers required for each space in the model.

(Expected time: 45 min)

1. File name to be used: *c08_office_fire_protections_tut1.rvt (M_ c08_office_fire_protections.rvt)*
2. File name to be assigned: *c08_Office-Space_tut1.rvt (M_c08_Office-Space_tut1.rvt)*

The following steps are required to complete this tutorial:

a. Open the *c08_office_fire_protections.rvt (M_ c08_office_fire_protections.rvt)* file.
b. Create pipe types.
c. Configure the pipe settings.
d. Create space schedule for estimating sprinklers.
e. Save the project using the **Save As** tool.
f. Close the project by using the **Close** tool.

Opening a Project

In this section, you will download the *c08_office_fire_protections.rvt (M_08_office_fire_protections.rvt)* file from *www.cadsofttech.com* and then open the file.

1. To open a file, choose **Open > Project** from **File** menu; the **Open** dialog box is displayed.

2. In the **Open** dialog box, browse to *C:\rmp_2019\c08_rmp_2019_tut* and then select the *c08_office_fire_protections.rvt* file (for Metric, select the *M_c08_office_fire_protections.rvt*). Now, choose the **Open** button; the selected file opens.

   Note
   *The architectural model named c04_archi_spaces_rmp_2018.rvt linked in this tutorial file is located in the c04_rmp_2019_tut folder. It is recommended to maintain the relative path to the architectural model. However, if the link is lost, you need to reload the file using the **Manage Links** dialog box which has already been discussed in the previous chapters.*

Creating Pipe Types

In this section, you will create new pipe types for the fire suppression system.

1. In the **Project Browser**, click on the "**+**" symbol on the left of the **Families** node to expand it.

2. In the expanded **Families** node, click on **Pipes > Pipe Types > Standard**; the **Standard** node is highlighted.

3. Next, right-click; a shortcut menu is displayed. From the shortcut menu, select the **Duplicate** option; a duplicate node with the name **Standard 2** is created and is displayed under the **Standard** node.

4. Select the **Standard 2** node and then right-click; a shortcut menu is displayed. From the shortcut menu, choose the **Rename** option; the existing name is displayed in an edit box.

5. In the edit box, type **Wet Protection-Fire** and press ENTER; the existing name is renamed, as shown in Figure 8-2.

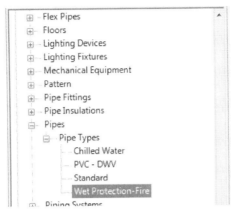

*Figure 8-2 The **Project Browser** displaying the **Wet Protection-Fire** type*

6. Next, ensure that the **Wet Protection-Fire** node is selected and then right-click; a shortcut menu is displayed. From the shortcut menu, choose the **Type Properties** option; the **Type Properties** dialog box is displayed.

7. In this dialog box, choose the **Duplicate** button; the **Name** dialog box is displayed.

8. In the **Name** edit box of the **Name** dialog box, type the **Dry Protection-Fire** text and then choose the **OK** button; the **Name** dialog box is closed and the **Dry Protection-Fire** type is displayed in the **Type** drop-down list in the **Type Properties** dialog box.

9. In the **Type Properties** dialog box, choose the **OK** button; the dialog box is closed. Notice that in the **Project Browser**, the **Dry-Protection-Fire** type is displayed under the **Pipe Types** head.

Configuring the Pipe Settings
In this section, you will configure the pipe types for the fire protection system.

1. Choose the **Mechanical Settings** button from the **Plumbing & Piping** panel of the **Systems** tab; the **Mechanical Settings** dialog box is displayed.

2. In the left pane of this dialog box, click on the **Conversion** node under the **Pipe Settings** node; various options related to the **Conversion** node are displayed in the right pane, as shown in Figure 8-3.

3. In the right pane, select the **Fire Protection Wet** option from the **System Classification** drop-down list.

4. In the **Main** area, click in the **Value** field corresponding to the **Pipe Type** parameter; a drop-down list is displayed.

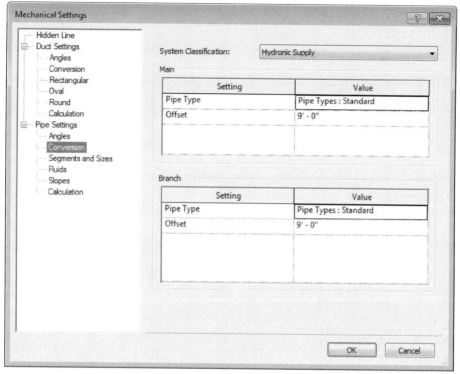

Figure 8-3 *Various options related to the* ***Conversion*** *node displayed in the* ***Mechanical Settings*** *dialog box*

5. From the drop-down list displayed, select the **Pipe Types: Wet Protection-Fire** option.

6. In the **Main** area, click in the **Value** field corresponding to the **Offset** parameter and replace the existing value of **9' - 0"** (**2750**) with **9' - 3"** (**2820**).

7. In the **Branch** area, assign the same settings as specified in the **Main** area.

 Note

The offset values specified for the main and branch pipes refers to the placement of the main and branch pipes with respect to the referenced level. Also, it is important to note that the branch offset allows you to automatically create branches that run above or below the main and other obstacles. This is useful for avoiding interference with pipes, duct, structural beams, or architectural components.

8. Now, repeat the procedure followed in steps 3 to 7 to assign the conversion settings for the **Dry Fire Protection** system. For creating the settings, use the following specifications:
    System Classification: **Fire Protection Dry**
    Pipe Type (Main and Branch areas): **Pipe Types : Dry Protection-Fire**
    Offset (Main and Branch area):   **9'3"(2820 mm)**

9. After configuring the settings for the pipes, choose the **OK** button; the **Mechanical Settings** dialog box is closed.

Creating a Space Schedule for Estimating Sprinklers

In this section, you will create a space schedule and find out the quantity of the sprinklers in the spaces.

1. Choose the **Schedules/Quantities** tool from the **Reports & Schedules** panel of the **Analyze** tab; the **New Schedule** dialog box is displayed.

2. In the **Category** list box of the dialog box, click on the **Spaces** category. Now, in the **Name** edit box, enter a new name **Space Schedule-Fire Protection**. Also, ensure that in the **New Schedule** dialog box, the **Schedule building components** radio button is selected and the **New Construction** option is selected from the **Phase** drop-down list.

3. In the **New Schedule** dialog box, choose the **OK** button; the **Schedule Properties** dialog box is displayed with the **Fields** tab chosen, as shown in Figure 8-4.

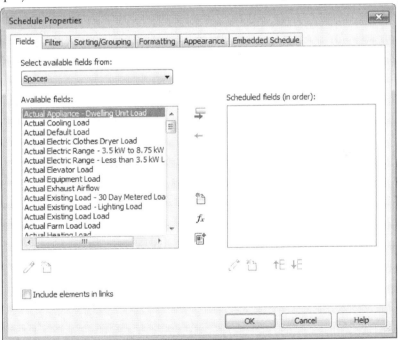

*Figure 8-4 The **Schedule Properties** dialog box with the **Fields** tab chosen*

4. In the **Available fields** area of the **Fields** tab, select the **Area** field. Now, press and hold the CTRL key and then select the following fields from the **Available fields** area: **Level**, **Name**, and **Number**.

5. Now, release the CTRL key and choose the **Add parameter(s)** button; the selected fields are added to the **Scheduled fields (in order)** area. Note that the added fields are selected and are highlighted in blue color, refer to Figure 8-5. Now, click on the **Number** field in the **Scheduled fields (in order)** area; other fields except the **Number** field get deselected.

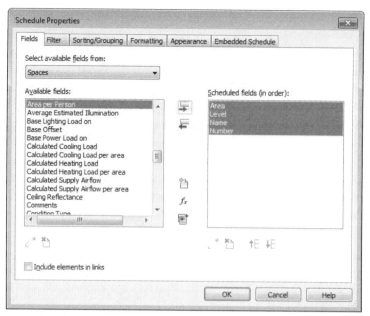

Figure 8-5 *The Schedule Properties dialog box displaying the added fields*

6.   Now, choose the **Move parameter up** button thrice; the **Number** field moves up in the order above the **Area** field. Similarly, arrange the remaining fields in the order **Name**, **Level**, and **Area** (Top to bottom), refer to Figure 8-6.

7.   Now, choose the **Add calculated parameter** button; the **Calculated Value** dialog box is displayed.

8.   In the **Name** text box of the dialog box, enter **Sprinkler Quantity- Min. Required** and then ensure that the **Formula** radio button is selected.

9.   Also, ensure that the **Common** and **Number** options are selected from the **Discipline** and **Type** drop-down lists, respectively.

10.   Now, in the **Calculated Value** dialog box, choose the browse button next to the **Formula** edit box; the **Fields** dialog box is displayed.

11.   In the displayed dialog box, select the **Area** field and then choose the **OK** button; the dialog box is closed and the **Area** field is added to the **Formula** edit box.

12.   In the **Formula** edit box, type **/130** (for Metric unit type **/12**) after the **Area** text to complete the formula as Area/130 (for Metric unit type Area/12).

      The fire protection code requires one sprinkler for every 130 square feet (sprinkler required for every 12 square meter).

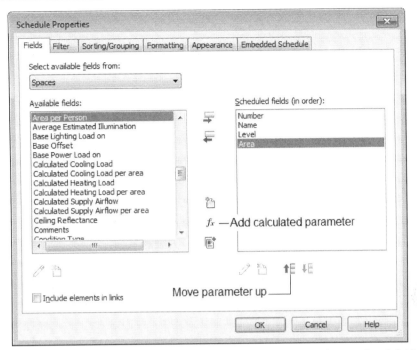

*Figure 8-6 The **Scheduled fields (in order)** area displaying the re-ordered fields*

 Note
*The formula that you enter in the **Formula** edit box is case sensitive.*

13. Now, choose the **OK** button; the **Calculated Value** dialog box is closed and the **Sprinkler Quantity- Min. Required** parameter is added to the **Scheduled fields (in order)** area.

14. Choose the **Filter** tab from the **Schedule Properties** dialog box; the options in this tab are displayed.

15. Select the **Level** option from the **Filter by** drop-down list and also ensure that the **equals** option is selected in the drop-down list displayed next to it.

16. Next, select the **Level 1** option from the drop-down list located at the third position corresponding to the **Filter by** parameter, if it is not selected by default.

17. Now, ensure that the **(none)** option is selected in the **And** drop-down list.

18. In the **Schedule Properties** dialog box, choose the **Sorting/Grouping** tab and then select the **Number** option from the **Sort by** drop-down list. Also, ensure that the **Ascending** radio button located next to it is selected.

19. Now, ensure that the **(none)** option is selected in the **Then by** drop-down list and then select the **Grand totals** check box. Ensure that the **Title, count, and totals** option is selected in the drop-down list displayed next to it.

20. Choose the **Formatting** tab. Next, in the **Fields** area, select the **Sprinkler Quantity- Min. Required** field; the right pane displays the information related to the selected field.

21. In the right pane of the **Formatting** tab, choose the **Field Format** button; the **Format** dialog box is displayed.

22. In the **Format** dialog box, clear the **Use default settings** check box and then select the **Fixed** option from the **Units** drop-down list.

23. In the **Format** dialog box, select the **2 decimal places** option from the **Rounding** drop-down list.

24. Now, choose the **OK** button; the **Format** dialog box is closed. In the **Formatting** tab, select the **Calculate totals** option from the drop-down list located below the **Show conditional format on sheets** check box and then choose the **OK** button again; the **Schedule Properties** dialog box is closed; the schedule is displayed in the drawing area, as shown in Figure 8-7.

<Space Schedule-Fire Protection>				
A	B	C	D	E
Number	Name	Level	Area	Sprinkler Quantity- Min. Required
101	CEO-Office	Level 1	156 SF	1.20
102	V.P. Marketing	Level 1	117 SF	0.90
103	Toilet-1	Level 1	70 SF	0.54
104	Rest Room	Level 1	97 SF	0.75
105	Cafeteria	Level 1	109 SF	0.84
106	Store	Level 1	84 SF	0.64
107	Purchase	Level 1	153 SF	1.18
108	International	Level 1	104 SF	0.80
109	H.R.	Level 1	130 SF	1.00
110	Central Area	Level 1	1015 SF	7.81
111	Quality	Level 1	160 SF	1.23
112	Open	Level 1	157 SF	1.21
113	Conference-2	Level 1	216 SF	1.66
114	Conference	Level 1	201 SF	1.55
115	Lounge	Level 1	844 SF	6.49
116	Meeting Room	Level 1	106 SF	0.81
117	Service	Level 1	84 SF	0.64
118	Shaft	Level 1	63 SF	0.49
119	Services	Level 1	75 SF	0.57
120	Accounts	Level 1	145 SF	1.11

*Figure 8-7 The **Scheduled fields** area displaying the re-ordered fields*

You can refer to the minimum number of sprinklers per space data as you place sprinklers in order to satisfy the design and code requirements. Although, you rounded the data to 2 decimal places, you will want to round all the decimals up to the next whole number.

 Note

A schedule in Revit is not only a construction document but also a design tool. When you change editable entries in the schedule to modify your system, you are actually editing information in a database of building information. As a result, each change is dynamic and is reflected throughout your project.

Saving the Project

In this section, you need to save the project and settings using the **Save As** tool.

1. To save the project with the specified settings, choose **Save As > Project** from **File Menu**. As you are saving the project for the first time, the **Save As** dialog box is displayed.

2. In this dialog box, browse to *C:\rmp_2019\c08_rmp_2019_tut* and then in the **File name** edit box, enter **c08_Office-Space_tut1** (for Metric **M_c08_Office-Space_tut1**).

3. In the displayed dialog box, choose the **Save** button to save the current project file with the specified name and to close the **Save As** dialog box.

Closing the Project

1. To close the project, choose the **Close** option from the **File** menu.

EXERCISE

Exercise 1	Fire Protection System

Download the *c08_Conference-Center_exer1.rvt* file from *http://www.cadsofttechcom*. The path of the file is as follows: *Textbooks > Civil/GIS > Revit MEP > Revit MEP 2019 For Novices*.

Open the *c08_Conference-Center_exer1.rvt* file and create a fire protection system in the conference room for the *Conference-Center* project. For location of the room, refer to Figure 8-8. While creating the fire protection system, you will add sprinklers and then create a wet pipe system, as shown in Figure 8-9.

1. Project view to be used :
                 Ceiling Plans > Mechanical > 1 - Ceiling Mech

2. Family type to be used:
   Sprinklers
For Imperial	Sprinkler-Pendent_Semi-Recessed-Hosted : 1/2" Pendent
For Metric	M_Sprinkler - Pendent - Semi-Recessed - Hosted : 15mm Pendent

3. File name to be assigned: *c08_Conference-Center_exer1a.rvt*

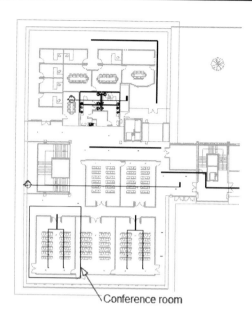

Figure 8-8 *The conference room for which fire protection system will be created*

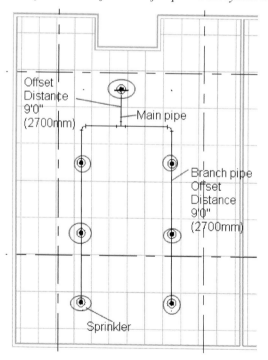

Figure 8-9 *The fire protection system created for the conference room*

Chapter 9

Creating Construction Documents

Learning Objectives

After completing this chapter, you will be able to:

- *Add dimensions*
- *Add text notes*
- *Use callout views*
- *Create drafting views*
- *Add sheets to a project*

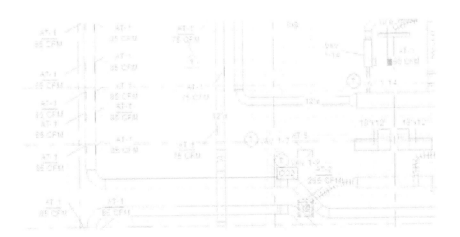

INTRODUCTION

In the previous chapters, you learned to create building envelopes, create different systems, analyze spaces, and more. In this chapter, you will learn to document a project and prepare it as a working drawing by using various tools and techniques in Revit. To document a system, you need to place dimensions in the plan view, add callout view, and place tags on ducts, equipment, machines, pipelines, and so on. In this chapter, you will learn various dimensioning terms and tools, tools for placing text notes, and the methods to place tags on elements in a project. You will also learn to add different views to the project, import and export views, and then add them to the sheets. Moreover, you will learn to prepare schedules and legends and to add them to the project sheets.

DIMENSIONING

Dimensions play a crucial role in the presentation of a project. Although the representation of MEP system in a project can convey how the appearance or design of the system would be, yet to materialize it at the site, there must be information and statistics regarding each element involved in the system. Since the design of a project is used for the actual assembly of the project, it is essential to describe each element of the project in terms of actual measurement parameters such as length, width, height, angle, radius, diameter, and so on. All these information can be added to a project by using dimensions. In most cases, information conveyed through dimensions is as important as the project view itself. The dimensions added to the project view ensure that the project drawings in the view are read and interpreted in an appropriate manner. Adding dimensions also helps in avoiding the discrepancies that may creep in between the elements used for generating the system drawings. In an MEP project, you can add dimensions based on the actual dimensions of the elements to be created. In other words, they are as real as the project elements themselves. The units used in the dimensions play an important role in describing the detailing that is required to complete a project. For example, the use of fractional inches in the dimensions indicates the amount of detailing required while generating a design. It also reflects the extent of detailing and the precision required to complete a project. Therefore, dimensions are used not only for specifying the sizes of elements, but also for guiding the people involved in the project, such as cost estimators, project managers, site engineers, contractors, supervisors, and so on.

Types of Dimensions

In Revit, you can create two types of dimensions for an element: temporary dimension and permanent dimension. Temporary dimensions appear while creating or selecting an element, but they do not appear in the project views. On the other hand, permanent dimensions appear in the views in which they are created and describe the size or distance of the elements. In Revit, you can add the dimensions denoting the length of elements such as ducts, pipes, cable trays, electrical conduits, and more. You can dimension the distance between them, arc length of a path made by them, angle between them, spot elevation of the level difference, and so on. While dimensioning a system, you can change various type parameters of the dimension such as its size, color, and so on by using the **Type Properties** dialog box. In the next section, you will learn about various entities in a dimension, various types of dimensions, adding dimensions to a project, and modifying the added dimensions.

The units that are specified in the initial start-up of a project are used by both the dimensions, by default. Unlike temporary dimensions, the permanent dimensions are view-specific. It means if you change the view of a project, the permanent dimensions will not be visible.

Using Temporary Dimensions

Revit displays temporary dimensions around the component or element when you place or sketch it in a view. The dimension that appears dynamically while drawing and placing an element is called temporary dimension. This type of dimension is not view-specific and may appear in any view while drawing or selecting an element. Temporary dimensions help you position elements at the desired location and references. While sketching the lines of desired length at the desired angle instantly, temporary dimensions can help you speed up your drafting work.

A temporary dimension appears only in three situations. First, when you draw an element; second, when you select an element; and third, when you select or place a component in a project.

Adding Permanent Dimensions

Permanent dimensions are added for a specific measurement. In Revit, you can access various dimension tools from the **Dimension** panel in the **Annotate** tab, as shown in Figure 9-1. You can choose appropriate dimension type and dimension tool to add dimensions to an element. The dimensioning tools are discussed next.

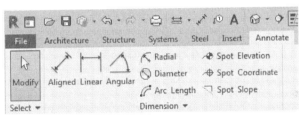

*Figure 9-1 Various dimensioning tools in the **Dimension** panel of the **Annotate** tab*

Tip
While working in a BIM project, dimensions are the primary data points to communicate the design intent. You can add dimension to plans, elevations and sections, detail and drafting views, as well as sheets. Dimensions are also used to create parameters for the objects in BIM.

Aligned Tool
Linear Tool
Angular Tool
Radial Tool
Arc Length Tool
Spot Elevation Tool
Spot Coordinate Tool
Spot Slope Tool

TEXT NOTES

In Revit, text notes are important part of a project detail. They not only help in adding the specification of various elements but also in conveying the specific design intent. Revit provides a variety of options to add text notes to different system detail views by using the **Text** tool.

Tip
In a BIM project, text notes are added to specify the detail of the model element or convey information regarding the drawing or its intent. Text notes are added to plans, elevation, sections, 3d views, detail views, and drafting views to improve the communication between various stakeholders of the project. However, you cannot add text notes to a camera view.

CALLOUT VIEWS

A callout view is an enlarged view of a part of a project model, which requires more detailing. Creating callout views is a common practice among engineers as callout views help them look at the project model more precisely and with a higher level of detail. For example, in mechanical discipline, a callout view can be used to show the details of a connection of a duct and a diffuser in the plan or an elevation view. In a project, you can create a callout view for a plan view, section view, or elevation view. In these views, the callout tag added in a view will be linked to the callout view. The view in which the callout tag is added is called the parent view of the callout view. If the parent view is deleted, the callout view will also be deleted. A callout tag is an annotation element that represents the location of the callout in the plan, elevation, or section view.

DRAFTING DETAILS

Drafted details are created when you want to access the details that are not referenced to the existing project views. These details are not linked to a building model and therefore, they do not update with it. To create a drafted detail, first create a drafting view and then use the drafting tools provided in Revit to sketch the details. You can also import in-built details from Revit's detail library and use them.

SHEETS

Ribbon:	View > Sheet Composition > Sheet

In Autodesk Revit, a sheet or a drawing sheet is a document set that is used for the final working drawings in a site. A drawing sheet contains sheet views that consist of multiple drawing views or schedules added in a project. Sheets are defined by a border and a title block. To create a drawing sheet, you first need to add a sheet view to the project and then add the required project views to the added sheet views.

TUTORIALS

General instructions for downloading the model file and performing the tutorials:

1. Download the *c09_rmp_2019_tut.zip* file from *www.cadsofttech.com*. The path of the file is as follows: *Textbooks > Civil/GIS > Revit MEP > Revit MEP 2019 For Novices*.

2. Next, browse to *C:\rmp_2019* and create a new folder with the name *c09_rmp_2019_tut*. Next, save and extract the file in this folder.

Tutorial 1   Office Space-Sheet

In this tutorial, you will create a callout view in the **B1 MEZZANINE** Architecture floor plan view of the *c09_Office-Space_tut1_tag.rvt* project file. Also, you will create a sheet and add different views in the created sheet.   **(Expected time: 45 min)**

The following steps are required to complete this tutorial:

a. Open the project file.
        For Imperial   *c09_Office-Space_tut1_tag.rvt*
        For Metric   *M_c09_Office-Space_tut1_tag.rvt*
b. Create a callout view.
c. Create a sheet.
d. Add project views to the sheet.
e. Save the project by using the **Save As** tool.
f. Close the project by using the **Close** tool.

Opening the Project file

In this section, you will open the project file created in Tutorial 1 of Chapter 9.

1. Choose **Open > Project** from the **File** menu; the **Open** dialog box is displayed.

2. In this dialog box, browse to *C:\rmp_2019\c09_rmp_2019_tut* location and choose the project file.
        For Imperial   *c09_Office-Space_tut1_tag.rvt*
        For Metric   *M_c09_Office-Space_tut1_tag.rvt*
3. Choose the **Open** button in this dialog box; the selected project file opens in the drawing window.

Creating a Callout View

In this section, you will create a callout view.

1. Double-click on the **B1 MEZZANINE** node under the **Floor Plans > Architectural** head of the **Project Browser**; the **B1 MEZZANINE** mechanical plan is displayed.

2. Invoke the **Rectangle** tool from the **Callout** drop-down in the **Create** panel of the **View** tab; the **Modify | Callout** contextual tab is displayed.

3. In the **View Control Bar**, select the **1/2" = 1'-0"** option for Imperial or select the **1: 20** option for Metric from the **Scale** drop-down list.

4. Next, select the **Detail View : Detail** option from the **Type Selector** drop-down list in the **Properties** palette.

5. Now, create callout by clicking at its first corner and the diagonally opposite corner, as shown in Figure 9-2; a rectangular callout is created.

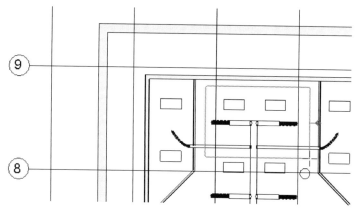

Figure 9-2 *The reference points for creating the callout*

6. After creating the rectangular callout, select it; the **Modify | Views** tab is displayed.

7. In the **Properties** palette of the selected callout, click in the value fields corresponding to the **Display Model** and **Detail Level** parameters and select the **Halftone** and **Fine** options from the drop-down lists, respectively.

8. In the **Properties** palette, click in the value field of the **View Name** parameter and enter **Duct Detail**. Next, choose the **Apply** button.

9. In the **Project Browser**, double-click on the **Duct Detail** node under the **Architectural** head of the **Detail Views (Detail)** node to display the callout view, as shown in Figure 9-3.

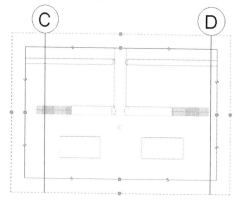

Figure 9-3 *Detailed view of the created callout view*

Creating a Sheet

In this section, you will create a sheet in the project.

1. Choose the **Sheet** tool from the **Sheet Composition** panel in the **View** tab; the **New Sheet** dialog box is displayed.

2. In this dialog box, choose the **Load** button and load the specified title block **C 17 x 22 Horizontal** from the **US Imperial > Titleblocks** folder or load the specified title block **A2 metric** from the **US Metric > Titleblocks** folder. On doing so, the specified title block is added and selected in the list of the **Select titleblocks** region of the **New Sheet** dialog box, as shown in Figure 9-4.

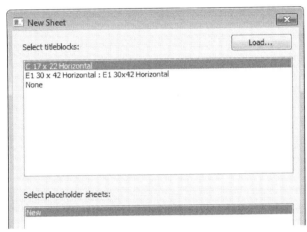

Figure 9-4 *Partial view of the* **New Sheet** *dialog box with the sheet loaded*

3. Choose the **OK** button from the **New Sheet** dialog box to create the sheet view by using the loaded title block. The added sheet is now displayed in the drawing window.

Adding Project Views to the Sheet

In this section, you need to add the specified project views to the sheet by dragging their name from the **Project Browser**. Further, based on the sheet layout, you need to place the project views at their designated place in the sheet.

1. In the **Project Browser**, click on the **B1 MEZZANINE** node under the **Architectural** head. Next, in the **Properties** palette, click in the value field corresponding to the **View Scale** parameter and select the **1/32" = 1'-0"** option for Imperial or select the **1:500** option for Metric from the drop-down list displayed.

2. In the **Project Browser**, press and hold the left mouse button on the **B1 MEZZANINE** node and then drag the view into the drawing sheet. Release the left mouse button when the project view appears as a rectangle in the sheet.

3. Move the cursor to the lower left area of the title block such that the corner of the rectangle is close to the lower left corner of the drawing sheet. Next, click to place the view; the **B1 MEZZANINE** architectural plan view is added to the sheet and appears enclosed in a rectangle, as shown in Figure 9-5.

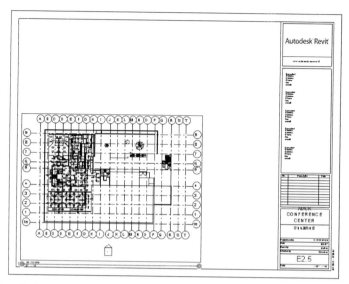

Figure 9-5 *The location of the **B1 MAZZANINE** architectural plan view in the sheet*

4. Next, ensure that the viewport of the **B1 MEZZANINE** architectural plan view is selected in the sheet. In the **Properties** palette, clear the check box corresponding to the **Crop Region Visible** parameter, if it is selected.

5. Choose the **Edit Type** button in the **Properties** palette; the **Type Properties** dialog box is displayed. In the **Type Properties** dialog box, ensure that the **View Title** option for Imperial and the **M_View Title** option for Metric is selected in the **Title** drop-down list.

6. Clear the check box corresponding to the **Show Extension Line** parameter and then choose the **Apply** and **OK** buttons; the **Type Properties** dialog box is closed.

7. Right-click in the drawing window and then choose the **Activate View** option from the shortcut menu displayed.

8. Now, in the project view, click on the elevation arrow head in the viewport below the drawing and right-click; a shortcut menu is displayed. Choose **Hide in View > Category** from the menu.

9. Again, right-click and then choose the **Pan Active View** option from the shortcut menu displayed; a move icon is displayed with the cursor.

10. In the sheet, press and drag the **B1 MEZZANINE** plan view and then place it at the location shown in Figure 9-6.

11. Next, right-click and choose the **Deactivate View** option from the shortcut menu displayed.

12. Click on the **Duct Detail** node under the **Architectural** head of the **Detail Views (Detail)** node in the **Project Browser** and then drag it to the sheet. Next, in the **Properties** palette click in the value field corresponding to the **View Scale** parameter and select the **1/16"=1'** option for Imperial and **1:200** for metric from the drop-down list displayed.

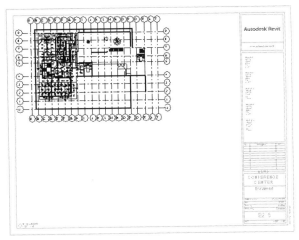

Figure 9-6 *Modified location of the **B1 MEZZANINE** architectural plan view*

13. Now, release the mouse button and click at any point to place the **Duct Detail** view, as shown in Figure 9-7.

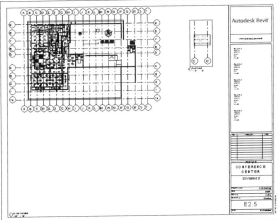

Figure 9-7 *Sheet displaying the detail view of duct*

14. Click on the **B1_HVAC DUCTWORK** node under the **Mechanical** head and then specify the value of the **View Scale** parameter as **1/32" = 1'-0"** for Imperial or **1:500** for Metric. Next, drag the **B1_HVAC DUCTWORK** node from the **Project Browser** and place it at the location shown in Figure 9-8. The three views are added to the sheet.

Note
*For better formatting, select the title block of the **B1 MEZZANINE** view and place it at a suitable location.*

Saving the Project

In this section, you will save the project file by using the **Save As** tool.

1. Choose **Save As > Project** from the **File** menu; the **Save As** dialog box is displayed.

2. In this dialog box, browse to *C:\rmp_2019\c09* and then enter **c09_Office-Space_tut1_sheet.rvt** for Imperial or **M_c09_Office-Space_tut1_sheet.rvt** for Metric in the **File name** edit box.

3. Now, choose the **Save** button; the **Save As** dialog box closes and the project file is saved.

Closing the Project

1. Choose the **Close** option from the **File** menu.

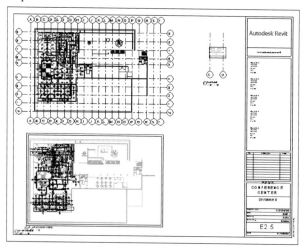

Figure 9-8 Sheet displaying all the added plan views

EXERCISE

Exercise 1   Conference Hall

Download the *c09_Conference-hall_exer1.rvt* file from *http://www.cadsofttech.com*. The path of the file is as follows: *Textbooks > Civil/GIS > Revit MEP > Exploring Autodesk Revit 2019 for MEP*. Now add callout view and add tags to ducts and diffusers at the **1ST FLOOR-HVAC DUCT** mechanical floor plan view of the downloaded file. Also. add space tags to the **1ST FLOOR-HVAC DUCT** mechanical floor plan view. Refer to Figures 9-9 and 9-10 to complete the exercise.   **(Expected time: 1 hr)**

1. Add callout view to the **1ST FLOOR-HVAC DUCT** mechanical plan view.
2. Add tags to round ducts in the **1ST FLOOR-HVAC DUCT** mechanical plan view.
3. Add tag to air diffusers in the **1ST FLOOR-HVAC DUCT** mechanical plan view.
4. Add space tag to **1ST FLOOR-HVAC DUCT** mechanical plan view.
5. File name to be assigned:

           For Imperial   *c09_Conference-hall_exer1a.rvt*
           For Metric   *M_c09_Conference-hall_exer1a.rvt*

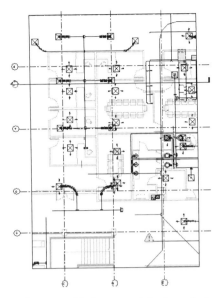

Figure 9-9 *The tags added to round ducts and air diffusers*

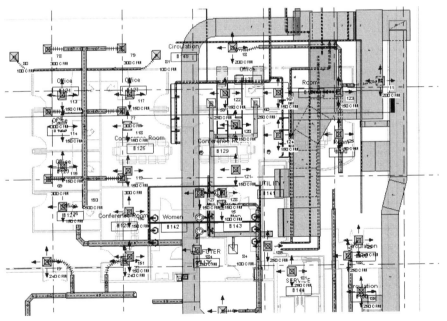

Figure 9-10 *The space tags added to the **1ST FLOOR-HVAC DUCTS** mechanical plan view*

This page is intenionally left blank

Chapter 10

Creating Families and Worksharing

Learning Objectives

After completing this chapter, you will be able to:
- *Create massing in Conceptual Mass Environment*
- *Create massing in Family Editor Environment*
- *Create massing in Project Environment*
- *Understand worksharing*
- *Understand Worksharing Monitor*

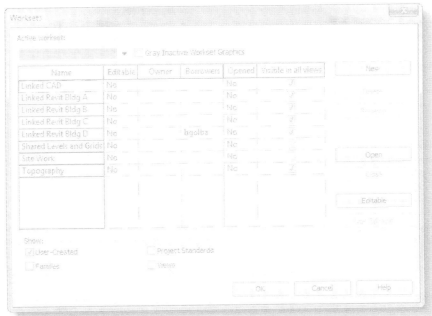

INTRODUCTION TO MASSING

In earlier chapters, you learned to use different system elements and components to create an MEP model. These system elements are parametrically associated and enable you to generate an MEP model based on specific design requirements such as duct types, cable trays, plumbing fittings, width, spaces, and so on. Each of the elements must be assigned specific properties to achieve the desired element parameters, thereby making system model accurate. Needless to say, this is a fairly time-consuming procedure. Autodesk Revit provides you an easy alternative to create system elements, known as massing.

UNDERSTANDING MASSING CONCEPTS

At the conceptualization stage of a project, you may need to study it in terms of its spaces, volumes, and shapes. You may also require to convey the basic idea of the structure of a building in a three-dimensional form without much detailing. This can be achieved using various tools which are used to create massing geometries.

The tools for creating massing geometry not only enable you to conceive and create a variety of system elements, shapes, and volumes with relative ease but also convey the potential design in terms of component masses and geometric shapes. You can create and edit geometric shapes and amalgamate them to form a complete MEP system. This process can be compared to the creation of element model using foam blocks. You have the freedom of choice to add or cut geometric shapes and join different blocks or masses to form an assembly. Figure 10-1 shows a group of volumes that can be created to represent the water closet of a plumbing fixture.

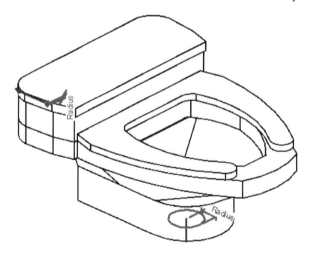

Figure 10-1 *Water closet created using the massing geometry*

CREATING THE MASSING GEOMETRY

In Autodesk Revit, you can create the massing geometry in any of these three environments: Family Editor, Conceptual Design, and Project.

To create the massing geometry in the Family Editor environment, choose **New > Family** from the **File** menu; the **New Family - Select Template File** dialog box will be displayed. In this dialog box, choose the *Generic Model.rft* file (commonly used) from the **English_I** folder, as shown in Figure 10-2, and then choose the **Open** button; a new file will open in the Family Editor environment. In the new file, you can create the massing geometry using various tools available in the ribbon.

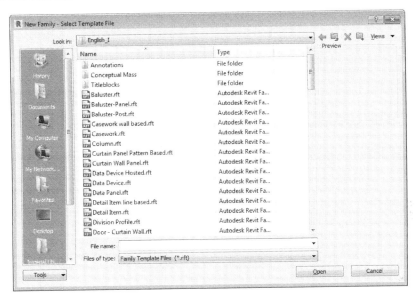

*Figure 10-2 Selecting a file from the **New Family- Select Template File** dialog box*

Creating a Massing Geometry in the Family Editor

As discussed earlier, the Family Editor environment provides tools to create massing geometry. To create a new mass, choose **New > Family** from the **File** menu; the **New Family - Select Template File** dialog box will be displayed. In this dialog box, select the *Generic Model.rft* file (commonly used) from the **English_I** folder and choose **Open**; a new file will open using the selected template file.

In the Family Editor environment, the **Create** tab contains tools to create massing geometry. These tools can be used to create massing geometries in a solid or in a void form.

To create a solid form, you can use a tool depending on your requirement, such as **Extrusion** / **Blend** / **Revolve** / **Sweep** / **Swept Blend** tool from the **Forms** panel of the **Create** tab. These tools are used to create different solid forms. Similarly, to create a void form, choose the **Void Extrusion** / **Void Blend** / **Void Revolve** / **Void Sweep** / **Void Swept Blend** tool from the **Void Forms** drop-down in the **Forms** panel. You can create a massing geometry using any of these massing tools or a combination of the **Solid** and **Void** tools. However, a designer can select the appropriate tool judiciously depending on the massing geometry to be created. The procedure of creating solid or void geometries using the tools in the Family Editor environment are as follows.

Creating an Extrusion
Creating a Revolved Geometry
Creating a Sweep
Creating a Blend
Creating a Swept Blend

Creating the In-Place Mass in a Project

In the Project environment, you have the option to create an in-place massing geometry by using the **In-Place Mass** tool. Invoke this tool from the **Conceptual Mass** panel of the **Massing & Site** tab; the **Name** dialog box will be displayed. In this dialog box, enter the name of the mass in the **Name** edit box and choose **OK**; the **Create** tab will be displayed. You can use the options in this tab to sketch the massing profile and convert it into a solid or void form. To sketch the profile for the mass, choose the **Model** tool from the **Draw** panel; the **Modify | Place Lines** tab will be displayed. You can use various sketching tools available in the **Draw** panel of this tab. While sketching, you can also use the **Reference Plane** tool from the **Draw** panel to draw references for the sketch. After sketching the profile, you can use any of the tools displayed in the **Create Form** drop-down in the **Form** panel. The **Create Form** drop-down displays two tools: **Solid Form** and **Void Form**. You can use the **Solid Form** tool to create a solid form and the **Void Form** tool to create a void form. To use any of the tools from the **Create Form** drop-down, you need to select the sketched profile from the drawing and then invoke the **Solid Form** or **Void Form** tool; the **Modify | Form** tab will be displayed. Using the options in this tab, you can specify the settings to change the instance property of the mass created, divide the surfaces of the mass, and can modify the geometrical elements of the mass. You can change the instance properties of the massing geometry like material and visibility from the **Properties** palette. After changing the instance properties of the selected massing geometry, you can change the geometrical property of the surface by adding edges and profiles. The tools for changing the geometrical properties are: **X-Ray**, **Add Edge**, and **Add Profile**. You can invoke these tools from the **Form Element** panel of the **Modify | Form** (solid form) tab.

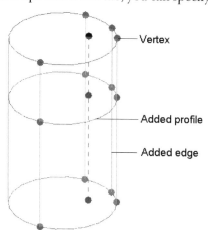

The **X-Ray** tool in the **Element** panel of the **Modify | Form** tab is used to display the geometry skeleton like vertices and edges of the mass. The **Add Edge** tool can be used to add edges to the form of the mass and the **Add Profile** tool is used to add profile to the surface of the mass. Figure 10-3 shows the added edge and profile in the **X-Ray** mode.

*Figure 10-3 Massing geometry with added edge and profile in the **X-Ray** mode*

MASSING IN CONCEPTUAL DESIGN ENVIRONMENT

Conceptual designing is the very first phase of a design process. The primary objective of a conceptual design is to create a representation of the idea for creating the system mass of a project. For creating a building project, the conceptual design is very important for architects, engineers, and designers as it helps in finding out the final representation of the design intent. Thus, it enables them to create a more specific sets of plans.

WORKSHARING CONCEPTS

Worksharing is a method of distributing work among people involved in a project to accomplish it within the stipulated period of time. In Worksharing, each person involved in the project is assigned a task that has to be accomplished through proper planning and coordination among the team members.

In a large scale project, worksharing is the most important method to finish the project in time and meet the quality requirements that are set during the process. Generally, in a large-scale building project, worksharing is based on the specialization of work. For example, professionals like Structural Engineers, Architects, Interior Architects, Electrical Engineers, Mechanical Engineers and Plumbing Engineers can contribute in their respective fields to accomplish the project. Each professional has his own set of work to perform for the accomplishment of the project. Therefore, worksharing is an important process that is needed to be implemented efficiently to complete the project in time.

TUTORIAL

Tutorial 1   Dual Duct VAV box

In this tutorial, you will create a Dual Duct VAV box in the conceptual mass family environment and then set various parameters to the VAV box created.

(Expected time: 1hr 30 min)

1. File name to be assigned:
   For Imperial   *Dual_Duct_VAV*
   For Metric   *M_Dual_Duct_VAV*
   The following steps are required to complete this tutorial:

a. Open the Family Editor environment for massing.
b. Create the VAV box body.
c. Create the VAV box outlet sleeve.
d. Create the VAV box inlet sleeve.
e. Create the VAV box control box.
f. Attach the outlet duct connector.
g. Attach the inlet duct connector.
h. Save the project.
i. Close the project using the **Close** tool.

Opening the Family Editor Environment for Massing

In this section, you will open the Family Editor environment.

1. Choose **New > Family** from the **File** menu; the **New Family- Select Template File** dialog box is displayed.

2. In this dialog box, select the folder **English_I** for Imperial unit system or **English** for the Metric unit system from the **Look in:** drop-down list. Next, select the template file:

    Imperial system: *Mechanical Equipment.rft*
    Metric system: *Metric Mechanical Equipment.rft*

3. After selecting the template, choose the **Open** button; the reference planes are displayed in the working area.

Creating the VAV box Body

In this section, you will create the body of the VAV box.

1. Make sure that you are in the **Ref. Level** view, if not, then double-click on the **Ref. Level** sub node under the **Floor Plans** node in the **Project Browser**. Next, choose the **Reference Plane** tool from the **Datum** panel of the **Create** tab; the **Modify | Place Reference Plane** contextual tab is displayed.

2. In this contextual tab, choose the **Pick Lines** tool from the **Draw** panel. Next, enter the value **2'** (**610 mm**) in the **Offset** edit box in the **Options Bar** and press ENTER.

3. Now, pick the vertical reference plane twice to create the two reference planes at a distance of **2'** (**610 mm**), one on the right and the other on the left of reference plane.

4. Next, enter the value **1'** (**305 mm**) in the **Offset** edit box in the **Options Bar** and press ENTER. Pick the horizontal reference plane twice to create two reference planes at a distance of **1'** (**305 mm**), one above and the other below the existing reference plane.

5. Choose the **Annotate** tab and then choose the **Aligned** tool from the **Dimension** panel.

6. Next, add dimensions to the created reference planes, as shown in Figure 10-4. Choose the **Modify** button to exit the dimension tool.

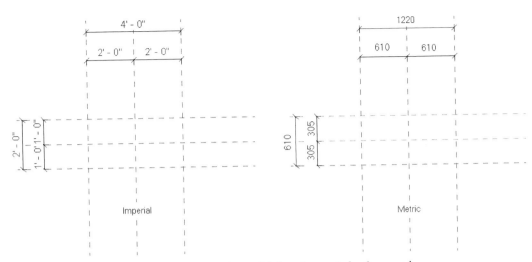

Figure 10-4 *Dimensions added to the created reference planes*

7. Select the **2'** (**610mm**) dimension line for the vertical reference plane; a blue **EQ** symbol appears. Click on the symbol; the dimensions are replaced by permanent **EQ** symbols.

Tip
The EQ symbol ensures that whenever there is a change in the position of one of the reference planes with equality constraint, the other reference plane moves symmetrically.

8. Next, select the **1'** (**305mm**) dimension line for the horizontal reference plane, and assign the equality constraint to it, as done in step 7, refer to Figure 10-5.

9. Select the **2'** (**610mm**) dimension line; the **Modify Dimensions** contextual tab is displayed. In this tab, choose the **Create Parameter** button from the **Label dimension** panel; the **Parameter Properties** dialog box is displayed, as shown in Figure 10-6.

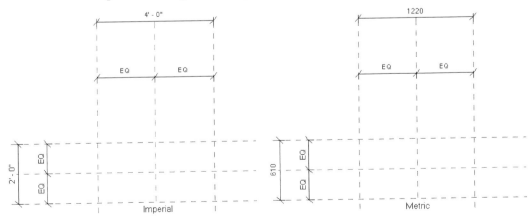

Figure 10-5 *Assigning equality constraint to the reference plane*

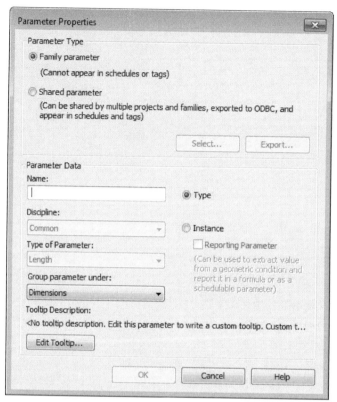

*Figure 10-6 The **Parameter Properties** dialog box*

10. In this dialog box, select the **Shared parameter** radio button in the **Parameter Type** area.

11. Next, choose the **Select** button in the **Parameter Type** area; the **Shared Parameter File Not Specified** message box is displayed, prompting you to choose one shared parameter. Choose the **Yes** button; the **Edit Shared Parameters** dialog box is displayed.

12. In this dialog box, choose the **Create** button in the **Shared parameter file** area; the **Create Shared Parameter File** dialog box is displayed.

13. Now, browse to the location **C:/rmp_2019** and create a new folder with name **c10_rmp_2019_tut**. Now, in the **File name** edit box, enter the name **Dual_Duct_VAV_box** for the Imperial system or **M_Dual_Duct_VAV_box** for the Metric system. Choose the **Save** button; the **Create Shared Parameters File** dialog box is closed.

14. In the **Edit Shared Parameters** dialog box, choose the **New** button from the **Groups** area; the **New Parameter Group** dialog box is displayed. In this dialog box, enter **Mechanical VAV box** in the **Name** edit box and choose the **OK** button; the **New Parameter Group** dialog box is closed.

15. In the **Edit Shared Parameters** dialog box, choose the **New** button from the **Parameters** area; the **Parameter Properties** dialog box is displayed.

16. In this dialog box, enter **VAV box Width** in the **Name** edit box. Select the **Common** option from the **Discipline** drop-down list and the **Length** option from the **Type of Parameter** drop-down list. Now, choose the **OK** button to close the **Parameter Properties** dialog box.

17. Repeat the procedure followed in steps 15 and 16 to create other shared parameters, as given in the table below. Refer to Figure 10-7 to view the added parameters.

Name	Discipline	Type of Parameter
VAV box Length	Common	Length
VAV box Height	Common	Length
VAV Outlet Width	Common	Length
VAV Outlet Height	Common	Length
VAV Inlet Diameter	Common	Length
VAV Max CFM	HVAC	Air Flow

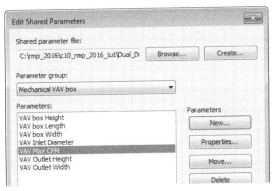

Figure 10-7 *Partial view of the* ***Edit Shared Parameters*** *dialog box displaying the created parameters*

18. Choose the **OK** button; the **Edit Shared Parameters** dialog box is closed and the **Shared Parameters** dialog box is displayed.

19. Now, select the **VAV box Width** option from the **Parameters** area of this dialog box. Choose the **OK** button in the **Shared Parameters** dialog box and then in the **Parameter Properties** dialog box to close them. Notice that the width label is assigned to the dimension line.

20. Next, select the **4'** (**1220 mm**) dimension line; the **Modify|Dimensions** contextual tab is displayed. Choose the **Create Parameter** button from the **Label dimesnions** panel of the **Modify|Dimensions** tab; the **Parameter Properties** dialog box is displayed.

21. In this dialog box, select the **Shared parameter** radio button and then choose the **Select** button in the **Parameter Type** area; the **Shared Parameters** dialog box is displayed. In this dialog box, select the **VAV box Length** option from the **Parameters** area.

22. Now, choose the **OK** button in the **Shared Parameters** dialog box and then in the **Parameter Properties** dialog box to close them. Notice that the length label is assigned to the selected dimension line.

23. Double-click on the **Front** subnode under the **Elevations (Elevation 1)** head; the view is changed to Front elevation. Invoke the **Reference Plane** tool from the **Datum** panel of the **Create** tab; the **Modify | Place Reference Plane** contextual tab is displayed.

24. Choose the **Pick Lines** tool from the **Draw** panel of the **Modify | Place Reference Plane** tab. In the **Options Bar**, enter **5"** (**127 mm**) in the **Offset** edit box and press ENTER.

25. Double-click on the existing reference level to create two reference planes, one above and one below it. Choose the **Modify** button to exit the selection.

26. Choose the **Annotate** tab and then invoke the **Aligned** tool from the **Dimension** panel. Next, add dimensions to the created reference planes, as shown in Figure 10-8. Choose the **Modify** button to exit the tool.

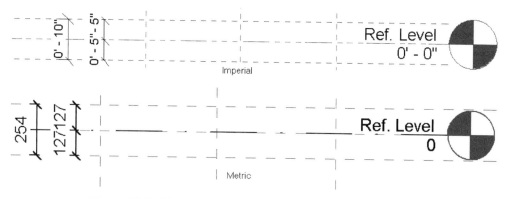

Figure 10-8 Dimensions added to the created reference planes

27. Select the **5"** (**127 mm**) dimension line; the **EQ** symbol appears with the selected dimension. Click on this symbol; permanent equality constraints are assigned to the created reference planes.

28. Next, select the **10"** (**254 mm**) dimension line; the **Modify|Dimensions** tab will be displayed. Choose the **Create Parameter** button from the **Label dimensions** panel; the **Parameter Properties** dialog box is displayed.

29. Repeat the procedure followed in steps 21 and 22 and assign the **VAV box Height** parameter to the VAV box.

30. Select the reference plane below the reference level, and then in the **Properties** palette, enter the name **VAV box bottom** in the **Name** edit box.

31. Next, invoke the **Set** tool from the **Work Plane** panel of the **Create** tab; the **Work Plane** dialog box is displayed. In this dialog box, ensure that the **Name** radio button is selected.

Then, choose the **Reference Plane: VAV box bottom** option from the drop-down list in the **Specify a new Work Plane** area, as shown in Figure 10-9. Choose the **OK** button; the dialog box is closed and the **Go To View** dialog box is displayed.

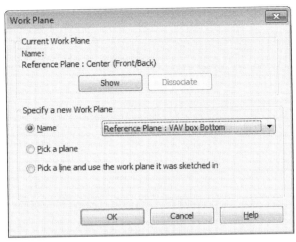

*Figure 10-9 Setting reference plane from the **Work Plane** dialog box*

32. In this dialog box, select the **Floor Plan: Ref. Level** option, if it is not selected by default, and then choose the **Open View** button; the dialog box is closed and the view is changed to plan view.

33. Next, choose the **Extrusion** tool from the **Forms** panel of the **Create** tab; the **Modify | Create Extrusion** contextual tab is displayed. In this tab, choose the **Rectangle** tool from the **Draw** panel. Now, make a rectangle with **2' x 4'** (**610 x 1220** mm) dimensions, and with the already defined reference planes, as shown in Figure 10-10.

34. Choose the **Finish Edit Mode** button to exit the tool and to finish extrusion. Next, make sure that **Extrusion Start** value is set to **0' 0"** (**0.00** mm) in the **Properties** palette. Then, choose the **Associate Family Parameter** button next to the **Extrusion End** edit box; the **Associate Family Parameter** dialog box is displayed.

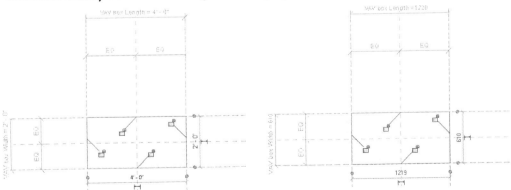

*Figure 10-10 Extrusion boundary created by using the **Rectangle** tool*

35. In this dialog box, select the **VAV box Height** option from the **Existing family parameters of compatible type** area, as shown in Figure 10-11. Next, choose the **OK** button; the **Associate Family Parameter** dialog box is closed. Notice that the end value **10"** (**254 mm**) is set in the **Extrusion End** edit box in the **Properties** palette. This value shows the height of the VAV box.

36. Next, double-click on the **View 1** subnode under the **3D Views** node in the **Project Browser**; the view is changed to 3D view and the model of the VAV box body is displayed, as shown in Figure 10-12.

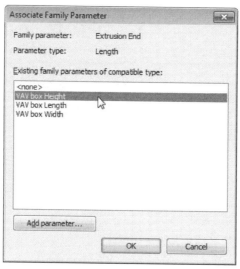

*Figure 10-11 Choosing an option from the **Associate Family Parameter** dialog box*

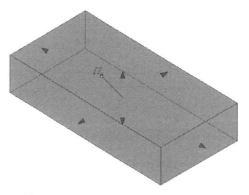

Figure 10-12 3D model of VAV box

Note
*If the view is not similar to the one show in Figure 10-12, you can choose the **Home** button near to the ViewCube.*

Creating the VAV box Outlet Sleeve
In this section, you will create the sleeve for the VAV box body.

1. Double-click on the **Right** subnode under the **Elevations (Elevation 1)** node; the view is changed to Right elevation. Next, choose the **Reference Plane** tool from the **Datum** panel of the **Create** tab; the **Modify | Place Reference Plane** contextual tab is displayed.

2. In this tab, choose the **Pick Lines** tool from the **Draw** panel. Next, enter **4"** (**100 mm**) in the **Offset** edit box in the **Options Bar**. Next, pick the middle vertical reference plane twice to create one reference plane on its right, and the other on its left.

3. Repeat the procedure followed in step 2 and make two reference planes, above and below the existing horizontal **Ref. Level**. Choose the **Modify** button to exit the tool. Next, annotate the created reference planes and assign the equality constraint to it, refer to Figure 10-13.

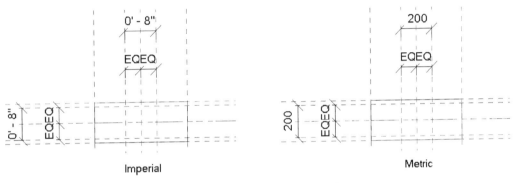

Figure 10-13 Annotating the reference planes

4. Now, assign the **VAV Outlet Width** and **VAV Outlet Height** parameters to the created reference planes following the procedure given in steps 20 through 22 of the previous section, refer to Figure 10-14.

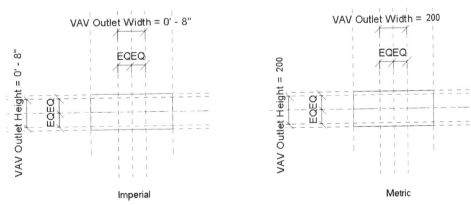

Figure 10-14 Parameters added to the reference planes created

5. Double-click on the **View 1** node under the **3D Views** node; the view is changed. Choose the **Set** tool from the **Work Plane** panel of the **Create** tab; the **Work Plane** dialog box is displayed. In this dialog box, choose the **Pick a plane** radio button from the **Specify a new Work Plane** area and then choose the **OK** button; the dialog box is closed.

6. Move the cursor on the right face of the VAV box body and then click on the face when it is highlighted, refer to Figure 10-15.

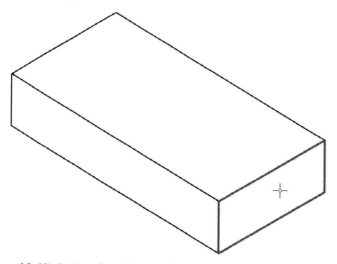

Figure 10-15 Setting the reference plane on the face of the VAV box body

7. Open the Right elevation from the **Project Browser**. Next, choose the **Create** tab and then choose the **Extrusion** tool from the **Forms** panel; the **Modify | Create Extrusion** contextual tab is displayed. Choose the **Rectangle** tool from the **Draw** panel of this tab.

8. Now, sketch a box with dimension **8"** x **8"** (**200 x 200** mm) box including the boundaries of the created reference planes, as shown in Figure 10-16. Make sure in the **Properties** palette, the value for **Extrusion Start** is **2' 00"** (**610 mm**). Next, enter the value **2' 2"** (**660 mm**) in the edit box next to **Extrusion End**. Choose the **Finish Edit Mode** button to finish sketching and exit the tool.

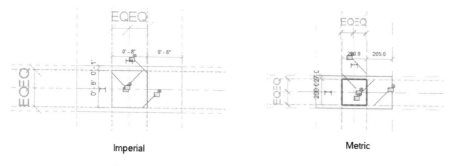

Figure 10-16 Sketching the VAV box sleeve

9. Choose the **Save As > Family** from the **File** menu; the **Save As** dialog box is displayed. In this dialog box, browse to *C:\rmp_2019\c10_rmp_2019_tut* and enter the name **VAV_box_Outlet_Sleeve** for Imperial system or **M_VAV_box_Outlet_Sleeve** for Metric system in the **File name** edit box. Next, choose the **Save** button; the dialog box is closed and the file is saved.

Creating the VAV box Inlet Sleeve

In this section, you will create VAV box inlet sleeve to the previously created body.

1. Choose the **Family Types** tool from the **Properties** panel of the **Create** tab; the **Family Types** dialog box is displayed, as shown in the Figure 10-17.

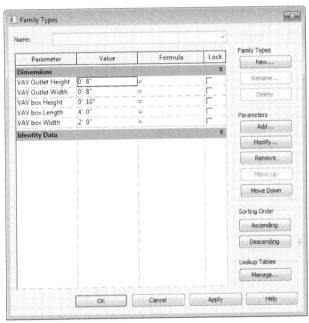

*Figure 10-17 The **Family Types** dialog box*

2. Next, choose the **New Parameter** button displayed at the bottom of the **Family Types** dialog box; the **Parameter Properties** dialog box is displayed. In this dialog box, select the **Shared parameter** radio button and then choose the **Select** button from the **Parameter Type** area; the **Shared Parameters** dialog box is displayed.

3. In this dialog box, select the **VAV Inlet Diameter** option from the **Parameters** area. Choose the **OK** button in the **Shared Parameters** dialog box and then in the **Parameter Properties** dialog box to close them. Next, in the **Family Types** dialog box, enter **4"** (**100 mm**) in the Value field for the **VAV Inlet Diameter** option.

4. Choose the **New Parameter** button from the bottom of the **Family Types** dialog box; the **Parameter Properties** dialog box is displayed. In this dialog box, enter **Inlet Radius** in the **Name** edit box in the **Parameter Data** area.

5. Now, select **Length** from the **Type of parameter** drop-down list and then select the **Other** option from the **Group parameter under** drop-down list in the **Parameter Data** area. Choose the **OK** button; the **Parameter Properties** dialog box is closed.

6. Now, in the **Family Types** dialog box, click in the **Formula** field located next to the **Inlet Radius** option and then, enter **VAV Inlet Diameter / 2**, refer to Figure 10-18. Next, choose the **Apply** button and then the **OK** button; the dialog box is closed.

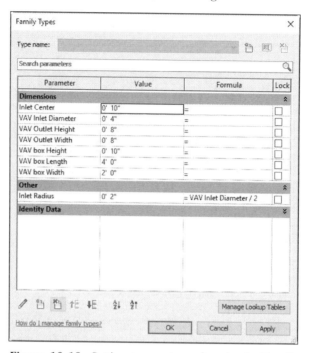

Figure 10-18   *Setting parameter values in the **Family Types** dialog box*

7. Double-click on the **Left** subnode under the **Elevations (Elevation 1)** node; the view is changed to Left elevation view. Now, choose the **Hidden Line** option from the **Visual Style** flyout in the **View Control Bar**; the VAV outlet sleeve disappears from the view.

8. Press and hold the CTRL key and select all the reference planes which define the VAV outlet sleeve. Next, choose the **Hide Element** option from the **Temporary Hide/Isolate** flyout in the **View Control Bar**.

9. Repeat the procedure followed in steps 1 and 2 of the previous section to make the two reference planes of dimension **5" (127 mm)** on either sides of the existing reference plane and assign the equality constraint to the planes created, refer to Figure 10-19.

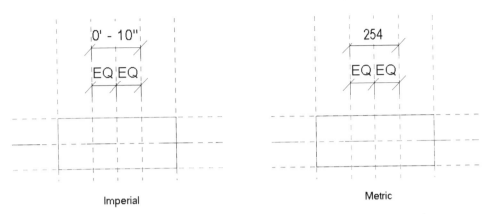

Imperial   Metric

Figure 10-19 Equality constraint assigned to the created reference planes

10. Next, select the **10" (254 mm)** dimension line; the **Modify|Dimesnions** tab is displayed. Choose the **Create Parameter** button from the **Label dimensions** panel; the **Parameter Properties** dialog box is displayed.

11. Enter **Inlet Center** in the **Name** edit box in the **Parameter Data** area, and then choose the **OK** button; the dialog box is closed and a label is assigned to the reference planes.

12. Double-click on the **Front** subnode under **Elevations (Elevation 1)** node in the **Project Browser**; the view is changed to Front elevation view. Next, select the first vertical reference plane from the left. Now, in the **Properties** palette, click in the **Name** edit box and then enter **VAV Inlet**.

13. Now, change the view to Left elevation view and choose the **Create** tab and then invoke the **Set** tool from the **Work Plane** panel; the **Work Plane** dialog box is displayed. In this dialog box, make sure that the **Name** radio button is selected in the **Specify a new Work Plane** area. Next, select the **Reference Plane : VAV Inlet** option from the drop-down list in the **Specify a new Work Plane** area, refer to Figure 10-20. Choose the **OK** button; the dialog box is closed.

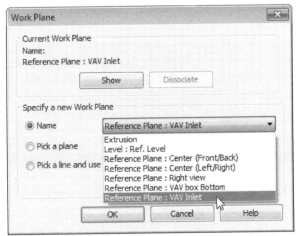

*Figure 10-20 Choosing the **Reference Plane VAV Inlet** option from the **Work Plane** dialog box*

14. Invoke the **Extrusion** tool from the **Forms** panel of the **Create** tab; the **Modify | Create Extrusion** contextual tab is displayed. Choose the **Circle** tool from the **Draw** panel of this tab. Draw two circles of **2"** (**50 mm**) radius at the intersections of the reference planes, as shown in Figure 10-21.

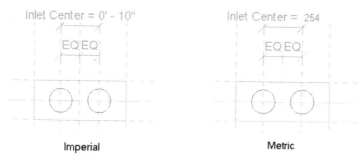

*Figure 10-21 VAV box inlet created using the **Circle** tool*

15. In the **Properties** palette, enter the value **0' 00"** (**0.00 mm**) in the **Extrusion Start** edit box and **-0' 4"** (**-100 mm**) in the **Extrusion End** edit box and then choose the **Apply** button to save changes. Next, choose the **Finish Edit Mode** button in the **Modify | Create Extrusion** contextual tab to finish the extrusion.

16. Change the view to Right elevation view and then choose the **Annotate** tab. Next, invoke the **Radial** tool from the **Dimension** panel. Next, add dimensions to the circles created and then press ESC to exit the tool.

17. Next, select both the dimension added to the circles and then choose the **Inlet Radius** option from the **Label** drop-down in the **Options Bar**. Repeat this step to assign label to both the circles, refer to Figure 10-22. Navigate to the 3D view. The geometry is created and it looks like shown in Figure 10-23.

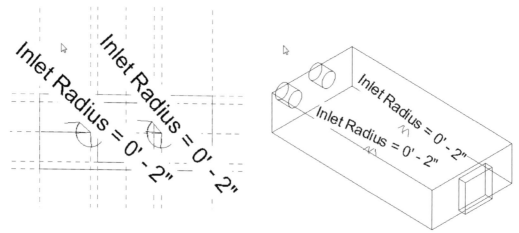

Figure 10-22 Labels added to the created geometry   *Figure 10-23 VAV inlet sleeve*

Creating the VAV box Control Box

In this section, you will create the control boxes to the model generated in the previous sections.

1. Invoke the **Set** tool from the **Work Plane** panel of the **Create** tab; the **Work Plane** dialog box is displayed. In this dialog box, select the **Pick a plane** radio button from the **Specify a new Work plane** area and then choose the **OK** button to close the dialog box.

2. Rotate the model and move the cursor to the Front face of the VAV box and then click when it gets highlighted, as shown in Figure 10-24. Now, choose the **Show** tool from the **Work Plane** panel of the **Create** tab; the created workplane is highlighted, refer to Figure 10-25. Choose the **Show** button again to make the highlighted work plane disappear.

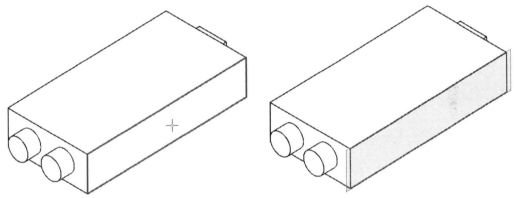

Figure 10-24 Setting work plane to the front face   *Figure 10-25* Showing the created work plane

3. Double-click on the **Front** view and then invoke the **Reference Plane** tool from the **Datum** panel of the **Create** tab. Next, choose the **Pick Lines** tool from the **Draw** panel. Next, enter **2" (51 mm)** in the **Offset** edit box in the **Options Bar** and then press ENTER. Pick the left reference plane to create a reference plane **2" (51 mm)** to its right, as shown in Figure 10-26.

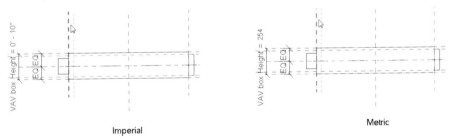

Imperial   Metric

Figure 10-26 Creating a reference plane using the **Pick Line** tool

4. Enter **1' 00" (300 mm)** in the **Offset** edit box. Next, pick the recently created reference plane to create a reference plane on its right. Now, choose the **Modify** button to exit the tool.

5. Choose the **Create** tab and then choose the **Extrusion** tool from the **Forms** panel; the **Modify | Create Extrusion** contextual tab is displayed. Choose the **Rectangle** tool from the **Draw** panel of this tab. Now, sketch a rectangle with **1'00"x0'10" (300 x 254 mm)** dimension including the boundaries of the created reference planes, as shown in Figure 10-27.

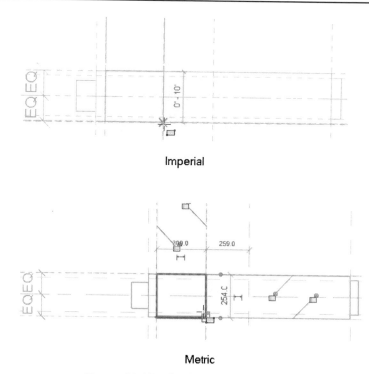

Imperial

Metric

Figure 10-27 *Sketching the extrusion boundary*

6.   In the **Properties** palette, click in the **Extrusion End** edit box and enter **1' 4"** (**406 mm**). Next, in the **Extrusion Start** edit box, enter **1' 00"** (**305 mm**), if it is not set by default. Next, choose the **Finish Edit Mode** button to finish sketching.

7.   Repeat steps 5 and 6 to create a control box on the Back elevation with **-1' 4"** (**-406 mm**) **Extrusion End** and **-1' 00"** (**-305 mm**) **Extrusion Start** values. The final 3D view of the created geometry is shown in Figure 10-28.

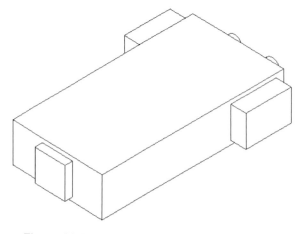

Figure 10-28 *3D view of the created control box*

Attaching the Outlet Duct Connectors

In this section, you will attach the outlet duct connector to the created geometry.

1. In the 3D view, navigate to the view in which the face of the outlet duct sleeve is visible. Next, invoke the **Duct Connector** tool from the **Connectors** panel of the **Create** tab; the **Modify| Place Duct Connector** contextual tab is displayed. Choose the **Face** tool from the **Placement** panel, if it is not chosen by default. Next, select the face of the VAV outlet sleeve to add connector to it, as shown in Figure 10-29.

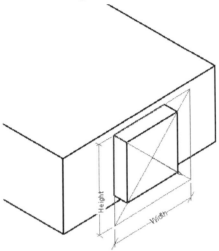

Figure 10-29 Duct connector added to the outlet duct sleeve

2. Choose the **Modify** button and then select the recently added duct connector. Next, click on the **+** sign next to the width dimension; the **Associate Family Parameter** dialog box is displayed. In this dialog box, select the **VAV Outlet Width** option and then choose the **OK** button; the **Associate Family Parameter** is closed and the parameter is added to the connector.

3. Repeat the procedure followed in step 2 and assign the **VAV Outlet Height** parameter to the height dimension.

4. In the **Properties** palette, click in the value field of the **Flow Direction** parameter and select the **Out** option from the drop-down list displayed. Next, click in the value field of the **System Classification** parameter and then select the **Supply Air** option, if it is not selected by default.

5. Choose the **Associate Family Parameter** button next to the **Flow** value field; the **Associate Family Parameter** dialog box is displayed. In this dialog box, choose the **New Parameter** button; the **Parameter Properties** dialog box is displayed. Click in the **Name** edit box in the **Parameter Data** area and enter **VAV Outflow**.

6. Choose the **Instance** radio button and then select the **Mechanical - Flow** option from the **Group parameter under** area, if it is not selected by default. Choose the **OK** button in the **Parameter Properties** dialog box and then in the **Associate Family Parameter** dialog box to close them. Choose the **Modify** button to exit the selection.

Attaching the Inlet Duct Connectors

In this section, you will attach the inlet duct connector to the created geometry.

1. Choose the **Family Types** tool from the **Properties** panel of the **Create** tab; the **Family Types** dialog box is displayed. In this dialog box, choose the **New Parameter** button from the bottom of the dialog box; the **Parameter Properties** dialog box is displayed. In this dialog box, enter **Duct Inlet Radius** in the **Name** edit box in the **Parameter Data** area.

2   Next, select the **Length** option from the **Type of parameter** drop-down list and the **Other** option from the **Group parameter under** drop-down list in the **Parameter Data** area. Choose the **OK** button; the **Parameter Properties** dialog box is closed.

3. In the **Family Type** dialog box, click in the value field of the **Formula** column of the **Duct Inlet Radius** parameter and enter the formula **Inlet Radius + 0' 1/16" (2 mm)**, refer to Figure 10-30. Next, choose the **Apply** button and then the **OK** button to save the changes and close the dialog box.

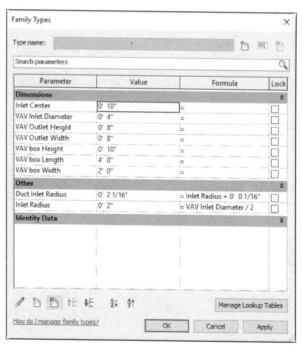

*Figure 10-30 Formulating the **Duct Inlet Radius** parameter*

4. Using the ViewCube in 3D view, navigate to the view in which the face of the inlet duct sleeve is visible, refer to Figure 10-31.

5. Next, invoke the **Duct Connector** tool from the **Connectors** panel of the **Create** tab and then choose the **Face** tool from the **Placement** panel, if it is not chosen by default. Next, select the faces of both the VAV inlet sleeves to add connectors to them, as shown in Figure 10-32.

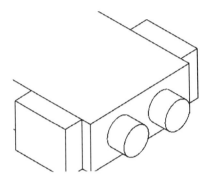 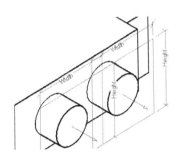

Figure 10-31 3D view of the inlet duct sleeve   *Figure 10-32* Connectors added to the inlet duct sleeves

6. Choose the **Modify** button to exit the tool and then select the recently added connectors. Now, in the **Properties** palette, click in the value field of the **Shape** parameter and then select the **Round** option from the drop-down list. In the **Flow Direction** parameter, select the **In** option from the drop-down list. Make sure that the **System Classification** parameter is set to **Supply Air**.

7. In the **Properties** palette, choose the **Associate Family Parameter** button next to the **Diameter** value field; the **Associate Family Parameter** dialog box is displayed. In this dialog box, select the **Duct Inlet Radius** option and then choose the **OK** button.

8. Choose the **Associate Family Parameter** button next to the **Flow** value field; the **Associate Family Parameter** dialog box is displayed again. In this dialog box, choose the **New parameter** button; the **Parameter Properties** dialog box is displayed. Click in the **Name** edit box in the **Parameter Data** area and enter **Inlet Flow**.

9. Select the **Instance** radio button and then select the **Mechanical-Flow** option from the **Group parameter under** area, if it is not selected by default. Choose the **OK** button to close the **Parameter Properties** dialog box and then the **Associate Family Parameter** dialog box. Choose the **Modify** button to exit the selection.

Saving the Project

1. Choose **Save As > Family** from the **File** menu; the **Save As** dialog box is displayed.

2. In this dialog box, browse to *C: \ rmp_2019/\c10_rmp_2019_tut* and then enter **Dual_Duct_VAV** in the **File name** edit box.

3. Now, choose the **Save** button; the **Save As** dialog box closes and the project file is saved.

Closing the Project

1. To close the project, choose the **Close** option from the **File** menu.

    The file is closed. This completes the tutorial.

EXERCISE

Exercise 1   **Supply Diffusers**

Create an air supply diffuser in the family editor, using the file *Mechanical Equipment.rft* for Imperial system or *Metric Mechanical Equipment.rft* for Metric system. Parameters to be used are given next. Refer to Figure 10-33 to 35 to create the model geometry.

(Expected time: 45 min)

1. Project File Parameters:
    Template File-

For Imperial	*Mechanical Equipment.rft*
For Metric	*Metric Mechanical Equipment.rft*

    File Name to be assigned-

For Imperial	*c10_Supply-Diffuser_exer1.rvt*
For Metric	*M_c10_Supply-Diffuser_exer1.rvt*

2. Dimension of the air diffuser:

Base dimensions:	2'x2' (600x600 mm)
Base geometry height:	6" (150 mm)
Top dimension:	1'6"x1'6" (450x450 mm)
Top geometry height:	3" (75 mm)
Connector radius:	6" (150 mm)
Connector height:	3" (75 mm)

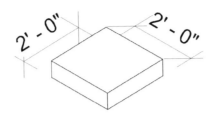

Figure 10-33 *The base geometry created*

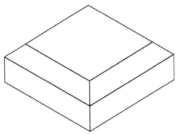

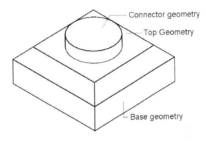

Figure 10-34 *The top geometry created on the base profile*

Figure 10-35 *Connector geometry created over the top profile*

This page is inetnionally left blank

Index

Made in the USA
Columbia, SC
06 November 2019